Collins

MATHS FRAMEWORKING

Complete support for Mathematics at KS3

YEAR 9 | **TEACHER'S PACK 2**

KEVIN EVANS   KEITH GORDON   TREVOR SENIOR   BRIAN SPEED

Contents

Introduction

This is the main teaching text for Year 9. It accompanies *Maths Frameworking* Year 9 Pupil Book 2 and caters for students working at Levels 5–7. Students who are working at Levels 3–5 are catered for by Pupil Book 1 and Teacher's Pack 1. Those working at Levels 7–8 are catered for by Pupil Book 3 and Teacher's Pack 3.

Maths Frameworking has been based totally on the finalised National Numeracy Strategy document. The detailed lesson plans deliver core material from the *Framework's medium-term plans*. We have reduced the teaching time from the 105 hours recommended in the NNS to around 85 one-hour lessons. This should enable teachers some flexibility to include tests, extended activities and revision classes in their teaching programme, and allows for the normal events that disrupt teaching time.

The lesson plans have the following features:

- **Framework objectives** to identify the key learning outcomes from the Framework
- Engaging **Oral and mental starter** activities to involve the whole class
- **Main lesson activities** to help you lead students into exercise questions
- **Plenary** guidance to round off the NNS three-part lesson
- **Key words** which highlight when to introduce Framework Vocabulary terms
- Extra **Homework questions** to consolidate and extend learning
- **Answers** for all pupil book exercises, homework and SAT-style questions

PLUS

The **free CD-ROM** that comes with each teacher pack allows you to extract text and graphics from the lesson plans, to help produce customised lessons for individualised teaching programmes. Diagrams can also be reproduced for use on overhead projectors or electronic whiteboards. Full details of how to use this resource are given on pages v–vii.

Chapter numbers and titles in *Maths Frameworking* follow the NNS medium-term plans. Due to the break caused by KS3 National Tests, the following specific approach has been taken to tackling the framework objectives in later chapters:

- **Chapter 12** is devoted to revision and is followed by two mock SATs papers, for practice prior to KS3 National Tests. Full answers and a tutorial section for the tests, suitable for individual student use, are provided on the CD-ROM.
- **Chapters 13 to 15** allow students to consolidate and extend knowledge of Handling Data and Shape, Space and Measures through a range of investigation tasks.
- **Chapter 16** consolidates Number and Algebra and prepares students for KS4 work.

The Oral and mental starters are designed to work with minimal specialised equipment – a blackboard and a piece of chalk would suffice – but resources such as OHPs, A3-sized target boards, counting sticks, number squares, student white boards and number fans make the activities easier to present and more accessible to students. A selection of inexpensive or free numeracy resources are available from Collins. See the accompanying website www.CollinsEducation.com/mathsframeworking for details.

The authors recognise that ICT provision in schools is varied and we have tried not to commit teachers to an activity that they could not carry out. However, suggestions for activities using ICT are included throughout the lesson plans and Pupil Book exercises. Some lessons also address cross-curricular issues such as Literacy and Citizenship.

The NNS is intended to improve standards. This can only be done by the good work of teachers in the classroom. The authors appreciate the good work teachers do and hope that *Maths Frameworking* proves a suitable resource to help them.

Kevin Evans, Keith Gordon, Trevor Senior and Brian Speed

Maths Frameworking
Year 9 Teacher Pack 2 CD-ROM

This free **Maths Frameworking Teacher Pack CD-ROM** provides all the pages of this pack in PDF format. These can be read by Adobe Acrobat Reader. If your computer does not already have the Acrobat Reader software it can be installed directly from the CD-ROM (please refer to the installation instructions below).
If your computer already has Acrobat Reader installed, follow these steps to view the **Maths Frameworking Teacher Pack CD-ROM**:

Macintosh
● Insert the Maths Frameworking Teacher Pack CD-ROM into your CD-ROM drive.
● Double-click the Maths Frameworking icon.

PC
For Windows:
● Click the 'Start' button and select 'Run'.
● Type 'D:\MF.pdf'. If you are not using the D drive as your CD-ROM drive, replace D with the appropriate letter.
● Click 'OK'.

Using the Maths Frameworking Teacher Pack CD-ROM

These pages contains brief guidance to help you to move around the CD, to enlarge and print pages and to adapt any of the activities to suit your own requirements.
For further, extensive help in using Acrobat Reader with the CD-ROM, select 'Reader Online Guide' from the 'Help' menu within Acrobat Reader.

Navigating the CD-ROM

Use the black, triangular direction buttons at the top of the screen to move forwards or backwards between pages of text.
You can also navigate your way around by clicking on the 'bookmarks' to each lesson, that appear on the left hand side of the screen. If a plus or minus sign appears to the left of a bookmark then you can click on this to show or hide subordinate bookmarks.

Printing the PDF pages

Select the print options you want by using 'Page Setup' in the 'File' menu. When you are ready to print, select 'Print' from the 'File' menu and specify the pages that you wish to print.

Adapting the text

You can select text or a graphic from the lesson plans and copy it to the Clipboard. Once the selected text or graphic is on the Clipboard you can switch to another application, such as a word processor or graphics package, and paste it into a new or existing document. (**Note:** *If a font copied from a PDF document is not available on the system displaying the copied text, the font cannot be preserved. Helvetica is substituted.*)

To select text and copy it to the Clipboard:

1 From the Tool Bar choose the Text Select icon.

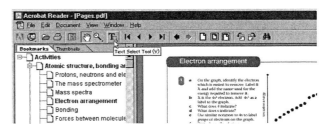

To select a line (or lines) of text, select the first letter of the sentence or phrase and drag to the last letter. To select a vertical section of text without selecting text on either side, hold down the Ctrl (Windows and UNIX) or Option (Mac

OS) key as you drag across the document. To select all the text on the page, choose Edit > Select All.

2 From the 'Edit' menu select 'Copy' to copy the selected text to the Clipboard. You can then view what you have selected by choosing 'Show Clipboard' from the 'Window' menu. (**Note**: *In Windows 95, the Clipboard viewer is not installed by default; therefore, you cannot use the Show Clipboard command until you install it. Install the Clipboard viewer by choosing Start > Settings > Control Panel > Add/ Remove Programs and clicking the Windows Setup tab. Double-click Accessories, check Clipboard viewer, and click 'OK'.*)

To select and copy graphics to the Clipboard:

1 Choose the Graphics Select tool by holding down the mouse button on the Text Select icon and dragging to the Graphics Select tool. Or press Shift-V as necessary to cycle through the group of tools. The cursor changes to a cross-hair icon.

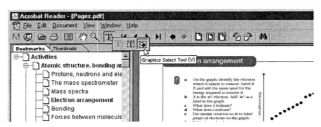

2 Drag a rectangle around the graphic you want to copy. To deselect the graphic and start over, click anywhere outside the selected graphic.

3 From the 'Edit' menu select 'Copy' to copy the selected graphic to the Clipboard. The graphic is copied in a WMF format for Windows, and a PICT for Macintosh. (**Notes**: *Copied graphics may include text, but text copied with this tool will not be editable by a word processor. Use the Text Select tool for any text you wish to be able to edit. In case of copied graphics being of low resolution, try zooming in, using the magnifying glass tool, to make the desired section appear as large as possible before selecting and copying it.*)

Adobe Acrobat Reader 5 software

Installation

Macintosh

● Insert the CD-ROM into your CD-ROM drive.
● Double-click the 'Install Acrobat Reader 5' icon that appears in the window.

PC

For Windows:
● Click the 'Start' button and select 'Run'.
● Type 'D:\acroread\rp500enu.exe'. If you are not using the D drive as your CD-ROM drive, replace D with the appropriate letter.
● Click 'OK'.
  Note that this is Adobe Acrobat 5 installer, but all files on this CD-ROM are compatible with Adobe Acrobat 4. Adobe Acrobat 5 will not run on Windows 3.1 or non-Power Macintoshes.

System Requirements

Macintosh

● PowerPC processor
● Mac OS software version 8.6, 9.0.4, 9.1, or Mac OS X
● 32 MB of RAM (with virtual memory on) (64 MB recommended)
● 150 MB of available hard-disk space

PC

● Intel Pentium processor
● Microsoft Windows 95 OSR 2.0, Windows 98, Windows Millennium, Windows NT 4.0 with Service Pack 5 or 6, Windows 2000, or Windows XP
● 32 MB of RAM (64 MB recommended)
● 150 MB of available hard-disk space

Help

When using Acrobat Reader, select 'Reader Online Guide' from the Help menu.

Attributions

Adobe and Acrobat are trademarks of Adobe Systems Incorporated.

Windows is a registered trademark and Windows NT is a trademark of Microsoft in the U.S. and other countries. Pentium is a registered trademark of Intel Corporation.

Macintosh and Power Macintosh are registered trademarks of Apple Computer, Inc.

Restrictions on use

Published by HarperCollins*Publishers* Ltd

77–85 Fulham Palace Road, London W6 8JB

© HarperCollins*Publishers* Ltd 2003

First published 2003

CHAPTER 1

Algebra 1 & 2

LESSON 1.1

Framework objectives – Sequences
Generate terms of a sequence using position-to-term definitions of the sequence, on paper and using ICT.

Oral and mental starter

- Put on the board 10^2 and ask: 'What does this represent?'
- You want the response 'Ten squared', as well as 'A hundred' and 'Ten times ten'.
- Then put on the board 10^3 and ask: 'What does this represent?'
- You want the response 'Ten cubed', as well as 'A thousand' and 'Ten times ten times ten'. You may even get 'One hundred times ten'.
- Now put on the board 10^4 and ask: 'What does this represent?'
- The response is now 'Ten to the power four' and 'Ten thousand'.
- Now jump to 10^6 and ask: 'What does this represent?'
- You are looking for 'Ten to the power six', and 'One million'.
- Next, put on the board 10^9 and ask: 'What does this represent?' 'One billion' is the response that you want.
- The put on the board 10^{12}: 'What does this represent?' 'One trillion' is the response that you want.
- Talk about the good use made of powers in this way to represent big numbers.
- Then ask them about 10^{100}: 'What does this represent?' This is a googol, but you are unlikely to get a response.

Main lesson activity

- Introduce a sequence, such as Arsenal scoring in every one of 43 matches. Ask whether they could predict what Arsenal would score in their next game.
- Of course they would not be able to predict it, although they might have a good guess.
- But there are sequences where it is possible to predict what the next number is and be able to explain the rules generating the sequence.
- Put on the board the sequence 1, 10, 100, … and ask what might the next number be.
- There are different possibilities, but the most obvious is 1000, followed by 10 000.
- Ask the class if they could give the next five numbers in the sequence.
- Then ask them to describe the sequence – multiplying each term by 10 to find the next term.
- Put on the board $2n + 7$ and explain that this is a rule describing a sequence. It gives every term in the sequence. All that is needed is to substitute the integers 1, 2, 3, 4, … .
- Get the class to generate this sequence: 9, 11, 13, 15, … .
- Notice how the sequence goes up in 2s and that the first term is $2 + 7$.
- Go through with the class the building up of the sequence with nth term $3n + 2$. This will generate 5, 8, 11, 14, … .
- Notice that the sequence goes up in 3s, the number in front of the n. Notice also that the first term is $3 + 2$.
- Show the class that this rule will also work for negative numbers.
- Go through the sequence with nth term $4n - 3$. This sequence is 1, 5, 9, 13, … .
- Now put on the board 9, 13, 17, 21, … and ask the class as to what the nth term is for this sequence.

- Ask the students for the reasons why they suggest various rules. Lead them to the fact that, since we are always adding on 4, the nth term will start with $4n$. Then see what has to be added to 4 to get the first term of 9. This will be 5. So the nth term will be $4n + 5$.
- Show the class the sequence 3, 8, 13, 18, … and ask what the nth term for this sequence is.
- They should be able to identify the first part $5n$ as 5 is added on each time.
- Ask what must be added to 5 to get the first term of 3. The answer is –2. So the nth term is given by $5n - 2$.
- **The class can now do Exercise 1A from Pupil Book 2.**

Exercise 1A Answers

1 a 17, 21, 25 b 23, 28, 33 c 30, 37, 44 d 28, 34, 40 e 38, 46, 54
  f 17, 20, 23
2 a 5, 7, 9, 11 b 5, 8, 11, 14 c 9, 13, 17, 21 d 14, 19, 24, 29 e 2, 5, 8, 11
  f 2, 7, 12, 17 g –1, 3, 7, 11 h –2, 0, 2, 4
3 a $4n + 2$ b $7n + 1$ c $23 - 2n$ d $36 - 4n$
4 a $8n + 35$ b $64 - 7n$ c $13n + 22$ d $9n + 58$
5 a $14 - 5n$ b $2n - 13$ c $3 - 4n$ d $3n - 18$
6 a $0.2n + 2.2$ b $0.3n + 1.4$ c $7.3 - 0.5n$ d $5.7 - 0.4n$
7 a $\dfrac{n}{(3n - 1)}$ b $\dfrac{(2n + 1)}{(5n - 1)}$
8 a $4n - 2$ b 198
9 a $2n$ b 100

Extension Answers

There are many different solutions to each part. The following includes one example of each:
a 1, 1.5, 2, 2.5, 3 b 0.25, 0.5, 0.75, 1, 1.25 c 2, 4, 6, 8, 10
d 5, 10, 15, 20, 25 e 2.5, 5, 7.5, 10, 12.5

Plenary

- Discuss with the class whether every sequence can be described as given here with an nth term.
- Ask them to suggest sequences where a rule as given here cannot be used.
- Ensure that they leave the lesson appreciating that this method of nth term will work only for sequences that have the *same* amount added each time.

Homework

1 Write down the first four terms of each sequence whose nth term is given below.

  a $3n + 1$ b $4n - 2$ c $2n + 7$ d $6n - 5$ e $2n - 9$

2 Find the nth term of each of the following sequences.

  a 5, 7, 9, 11, … b 2, 5, 8, 11, … c 11, 16, 21, 26, … d 5, 13, 21, 29, …

3 Find the nth term of each of the following sequences of fractions.

  a $\frac{1}{2}, \frac{2}{3}, \frac{3}{4}, \frac{4}{5}, …$ b $\frac{1}{3}, \frac{2}{5}, \frac{3}{7}, \frac{4}{9}, …$

4 Find the nth term of each of the following sequences.

  a 3.5, 5, 6.5, 8, 9.5, … b 5.1, 7.2, 9.3, 11.4, … c 3.6, 6.1, 8.6, 11.1, …

Answers
1 a 4, 7, 10, 13 b 2, 6, 10, 14 c 9, 11, 13, 15 d 1, 7, 13, 19 e –7, –5, –3, –1
2 a $2n + 3$ b $3n - 1$ c $5n + 6$ d $8n - 3$
3 a $\dfrac{n}{(n + 1)}$ b $\dfrac{n}{(2n + 1)}$
4 a $1.5n + 2$ b $2.1n + 3$ c $2.5n + 1.1$

LESSON 1.2

Framework objectives – Pattern spotting

Generate terms of a sequence using term-to-term and position-to-term definitions of the sequence, on paper and using ICT.

Generate sequences from practical contexts and write an expression to describe the nth term of an arithmetic sequence.

Oral and mental starter

- Draw on the board three measuring jugs labelled 1 gallon, 3 pints and 5 pints.
- Tell the class that the gallon jug is full.
- Ask if anyone knows how many pints here are in the gallon. There are 8 pints.
- Working in pairs, ask which pair can work out, using just the three jugs, how to divide the liquid into two equal measures of half a gallon (4 pints).
- The solution is as follows:
  - ○ From the full gallon jug, fill the 5 pint jug, leaving a measure of 3 pints in the gallon jug.
  - ○ From the 5 pint jug, fill the 3 pint jug, leaving 3 pints, 3 pints and 2 pints.
  - ○ Pour all of the 3 pint jug into the gallon jug, giving 6 pints and 2 pints.
  - ○ Pour the 2 pints from the 5 pint jug into the 3 pint jug, leaving 6 pints and 2 pints.
  - ○ From the gallon jug, fill the 5 pint jug, leaving 1 pint, 2 pints and 5 pints.
  - ○ From the 5 pint jug, fill up the 3 pint jug, leaving 1 pint, 3 pints and 4 pints.
  - ○ Now just pour the 3 pint jug into the gallon jug to leave 4 pints in the gallon jug and 4 pints in the 5 pint jug.

Main lesson activity

- Draw on the board a circle with a chord (any straight line from one part of the circumference to another).
- Ask how many regions there are in the circle. (There are two.)
- Now draw another chord in the circle, intersecting the first one, and ask: 'How many regions are in the circle now?' (There are four.)
- Build up a table of results while doing this, showing number of lines and regions.
- Ask the class if they can tell you the maximum possible number of regions when another chord is drawn.
- Many might suggest six due to the sequence starting 2, 4, … . Put the suggestions on the board.
- Now draw in the chord to intersect both chords already in the circle. Count with the class the number of regions. There are seven regions. Put this in the table.
- Now ask again: 'What is the maximum number of regions if I draw another chord in the circle?'
- Some may spot the pattern, which gives 11. If so, then get them to explain the pattern to the rest of the class. Show that this is true. The explanation is that 2 is added, then 3, then 4 and so on.
- Now ask if anyone can describe the term-to-term rule. Encourage class discussion here, and clarity of explanation. There may be a few good suggestions, all different from each other but still correct.
- The rule is:
     $T(n)$ = Term + n
  where the build-up is from the term immediately before.
- Explain this terminology: $T(n)$ is the nth term and Term is the term immediately before it.

- **The class can now do Exercise 1B from Pupil Book 2.**

Plenary

Key Words

☐ **prediction**

- Discuss with the class how good their predictions have been and whether they got better as the lesson went on.
- Explain that it is good to try to make a prediction as this means they are actually looking at the pattern, which should lead to a refinement in the rule being looked for.
- To get results from complicated situations, it is very often useful to create simple diagrams in order to look at the pattern.

Homework

Look at the following diagrams.

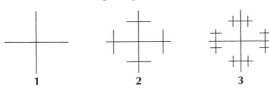

Diagram	1	2	3	4	5	6
Crosses	1	5	13			

a Before drawing a diagram, can you predict, from the table, the number of crosses in Diagram 4?

b Draw Diagram 4, and count the number of crosses there are. Were you right?

c Now predict the number of crosses for Diagrams 5 and 6.

d Check your results for part c by Drawing diagrams 5 and 6.

e Write down the term-to-term rule for the sequence of crosses. (**Hint:** $4 = 2^2$, $8 = 2^3$)

Answers
You will get the following results.

Diagram	1	2	3	4	5	6
Crosses	1	5	13	29	61	125

e $T(n) =$ Term $+ 2^n$

Oral and mental starter

- Ask the question: 'Is $1234 \times 5678 = 7\,006\,652$?'
- Is there a quick way of checking without doing the whole multiplication?
- One check is to look at the product of the last digit of each number: $4 \times 8 = 32$. The end digit of this number must be the end digit of the original sum. Here they are both 2, so we might be correct.
- Another check is to do the digit sum scan. That is, add the digits of 1234, 5678 and the predicted answer $7\,006\,652$, which gives us 10, 26 and 26.
- Add the digits of any numbers greater than 9, here giving us 1, 8 and 8.
- Now check that the product of the first two values is the same as the third value.
- Here they are the same – both 8 – so we might be correct.
- Try this out: 'Is $314 \times 783 = 245\,762$?'
- The digit sums come to 8, 9 and 8.
- The product $8 \times 9 = 72$, has digit total 9. This is different to the last digit sum, so the prediction is not correct.
- Let the class try this out with a calculator to convince them that this procedure always works.

Main lesson activity

- Put on the board $x \to 4x$ and ask the class whether they remember what this is. They should tell you that it is the function x maps to $4x$. Ensure that the class use the correct terminology.
- Put in a column underneath the numbers $x \to 1, 2, 3, 4$ and ask if anyone can tell you what each number will map to. You should get the response $1 \to 4$, $2 \to 8, 3 \to 12, 4 \to 16$.
- Now continue the diagram by making each term map back to itself. That is:
  $$1 \to 4 \to 1, 2 \to 8 \to 2, 3 \to 12 \to 3, 4 \to 16 \to 4$$
  Ask the class if they can tell you what function will map each back to where it started. You may need to hide the original column of numbers in order to focus only on the other two columns.
- You want to get the response $x \to \frac{1}{4}x$.
- Tell them that this is the **inverse function** of $x \to 4x$. Explain that the term 'inverse' here means doing the opposite process to return to the original values.
- Ask the class: 'What is the inverse of $x \to 5x$?'. You may need to go through this in the same way which you did for $x \to 4x$. Ask them to work out that the inverse of $x \to 5x$ is $x \to \frac{1}{5}x$.
- Discuss what is happening with the above inversion. That is, division is the inverse of multiplication and vice versa. Ask: 'When we see a pair of inverse functions, are they both inverses of each other?' You may need to refer to both $x \to 4x$ and $x \to 5x$ in order to show that this is true.
- Now put on the board the function $x \to x + 3$, and ask if anyone can propose what its inverse will be. Discuss each proposal and ask for a reason why the proposal was made.
- You need to lead the students to the inverse being $x \to x - 3$.
- Discuss with them the inverse of $x \to x + 7$, which is $x \to x - 7$.
- Now put on the board the function $x \to 4x + 3$ and ask for its inverse.
- This is not easy to see. You will need to break down the function into its two steps of $\times 4$ and $+ 3$. Show this in flow diagram notation as:

  $$x \longrightarrow \boxed{\times 4} \longrightarrow \boxed{+ 3} \longrightarrow 4x + 3$$

- Given that the inverse is the opposite process that returns the original values, the flow diagram needs to be looked at backwards. Reverse the arrows and start with x at the right hand side, to give:

$$\frac{(x-3)}{4} \longleftarrow \boxed{\div 4} \longleftarrow \boxed{-3} \longleftarrow x$$

- Remind the class that the inverse of × is ÷, and of + is −.
- This gives us the inverse function of:

$$x \rightarrow \frac{(x-3)}{4}$$

- Show that this is the inverse of $x \rightarrow 4x + 3$ by choosing a starting set of numbers, say, 1, 2, 3 and 4.
- **The class can now do Exercise 1C from Pupil Book 2.**

Exercise 1C Answers

1 **a** $x \rightarrow \frac{1}{2}x$ **b** $x \rightarrow \frac{1}{5}x$ **c** $x \rightarrow x - 6$ **d** $x \rightarrow x - 1$ **e** $x \rightarrow x + 3$ **f** $x \rightarrow 5x$

2 **a** $x \rightarrow \frac{(x-3)}{2}$ **b** $x \rightarrow \frac{(x-1)}{3}$ **c** $x \rightarrow \frac{(x+3)}{4}$ **d** $x \rightarrow \frac{(x+2)}{5}$ **e** $x \rightarrow \frac{(x-7)}{4}$

   f $x \rightarrow \frac{(x+5)}{6}$

3 Two different types of example are:

   i $x \rightarrow 10 - x$ $1 \rightarrow 9 \rightarrow 1$ **ii** $x \rightarrow \frac{12}{x}$ $1 \rightarrow 12 \rightarrow 1$

   $\qquad\qquad\qquad 2 \rightarrow 8 \rightarrow 2 \qquad\qquad\qquad\qquad 2 \rightarrow 6 \rightarrow 2$

   $\qquad\qquad\qquad 3 \rightarrow 7 \rightarrow 3 \qquad\qquad\qquad\qquad 3 \rightarrow 4 \rightarrow 3$

4 **a** $x \rightarrow \frac{(x-6)}{2}$ **b** $x \rightarrow \frac{(x+12)}{3}$ **c** $x \rightarrow 4x - 3$ **d** $x \rightarrow 5x + 2$ **e** $x \rightarrow 2(x - 3)$

   f $x \rightarrow 2(x + 7)$

5 **a** {2, 4, 6, 8, 10} **b** 2, 4, 6, 8, 10 **c** Yes

9 The lines are symmetrical about the line $y = x$

Plenary

Key Words

☐ **inverse**

- Ask: 'What is the inverse of multiplication?' (Division.)
- Ask: 'What is the inverse of addition?' (Subtraction.)
- Ask: 'What is the inverse of squaring?' (Taking the square root.)
- Discuss the problems that this last inverse has. For example, the square of a negative number is the same as the square of its positive value. So what about the inverse?

Homework

1 Write down the inverse of each of the following functions.

   a $x \rightarrow 3x$ **b** $x \rightarrow x + 8$ **c** $x \rightarrow 6 + x$ **d** $x \rightarrow \frac{x}{2}$ **e** $x \rightarrow 2x + 1$ **f** $x \rightarrow 4x + 3$ **g** $x \rightarrow 3x - 5$

2 Write down two different types of inverse function and show that they are self inverse functions.

3 Write down the inverse of each of the following functions.

   a $x \rightarrow 3(x + 5)$ **b** $x \rightarrow \frac{1}{2}(x + 5)$ **c** $x \rightarrow \frac{(6 + x)}{4}$

4 **a** On a pair of axes, draw the graph of the function $x \rightarrow 2x + 3$.

   b On the same pair of axes, draw the graph of the inverse of $x \rightarrow 2x + 3$.

   c Comment on the symmetries of the graphs.

   Answers

   1 **a** $x \rightarrow \frac{1}{3}x$ **b** $x \rightarrow x - 8$ **c** $x \rightarrow x - 6$ **d** $x \rightarrow 2x$ **e** $x \rightarrow \frac{(x-1)}{2}$ **f** $x \rightarrow \frac{(x-3)}{4}$ **g** $\frac{(x+5)}{3}$

   2 There will be a variety of different correct answers.

   3 **a** $x \rightarrow \frac{1}{3}x - 5$ **b** $x \rightarrow 2x - 5$ **c** $x \rightarrow 4x - 6$

   4 **c** The graphs are reflections of each other in the line $y = x$.

LESSON 1.4

Framework objectives – Graphs

Construct functions arising from real life problems and plot their corresponding graphs.

Oral and mental starter

- Ask: 'Who knows how many miles is equivalent to 8 km?' (5 miles)
- Use this fact to ask quick-fire questions about equivalences of the following:

Kilometres	16	24	32	40	64	80	96
Miles	10	15	20	25	40	50	60

- Discuss how they need to think: 'How many 8s? Then multiply that by 5.'
- Now ask for approximations, such as 10 kilometres and 60 kilometres.
- Again, look for approximations of eights. So, 10 km is just over 1 one eight which will make it just over 5 miles. For an approximation, call it 6 miles.
- For 60 kilometres, divide by 8, giving $7\frac{1}{2}$, which gives $5 \times 7\frac{1}{2} = 35 + 2\frac{1}{2} = 37\frac{1}{2}$. As this is an approximation, round to 38 miles.
- Finish off by trying mentally to convert approximately the following:

Kilometres	20	35	50	70	90	100	200
Miles	13	22	31	44	56	63	125

- As the concern is to find approximations, any answer 'close to the correct mileage' will be acceptable.
- The main intention is to practise mental division by 8 and multiplication by 5.

Main lesson activity

- Draw on the board a pair of axes with the horizontal axis labelled time and the vertical labelled distance.
- Ask: 'What might the graph look like if it were representing a car being driven at a steady speed?'(Straight line.) You may want to discuss that a steeper line represents a faster speed but you will need to create values for the graph in order to show this.
- Draw another similar pair of axes on the board and ask: 'What shape would the graph have if the car were slowing down?'
- The graph would be a curve that starts with a positive gradient then gradually becomes horizontal.
- Now draw another similar pair of axes on the board and ask what shape the graph would be for a car accelerating from standstill to a steady speed.
- This will show a different type of curve with a horizontal gradient that gradually becomes more positive then stays constant (a straight line) at the steady speed.
- Discuss with the class that the graphs illustrate typical speeds, but that in real life there would be a lot of changes in the speed of the car resulting in quite different graphs to the ones drawn.
- Tell the class how useful graphs can be and that they can hold a lot of information.
- Look at the graph in Pupil Book 2 page 10 showing a race between three boys. Ask the class to tell you the story behind the graph.

- **The class can now do Exercise 1D from Pupil Book 2.**

Extension Answers

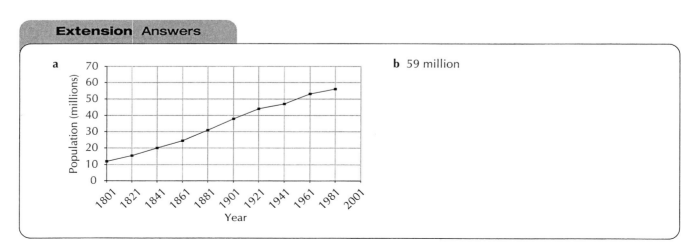

b 59 million

1 **a** 300m **b** 75m **c** 42 seconds **d** D: 40 seconds, E: 60 seconds
  e Rocket D went higher and hence travelled a greater distance vertically. The graph does not show any horizontal distance.

2 **a** Somebody got into the bath gradually whilst it was still filling **b** After 4 minutes
  c The more water in the bath, the quicker the water will empty out, it gradually slows down **d** 3 minutes

3 **a**   **b**   **c**   **d**

4 **a** C **b** A **c** B
5 **a** C **b** A **c** B
6 **a**   **b**   **c**   **d**   **e**

Plenary

- Draw on the board a pair of axes labelled time on the horizontal axis and distance on the vertical axis.
- Ask a student to draw on the axes a graph representing their journey to school that day.
- Discuss this graph and whether it actually shows the variances in speed, the stationary times etc.
- If time, ask someone to sketch a graph of an aeroplane journey from London to Amsterdam.

Key Words
- axes
- gradient
- acceleration

Homework

1 Sketch graphs to show how the depth of water varies with time when water drips steadily into the following containers.

  a   **b**   **c**

2 Sketch distance–time graphs to illustrate each of the following situations.

  a A car accelerating away from traffic lights.

  b A train slowing down to a standstill in a railway station.

  c A car travelling at a steady speed and then having to accelerate to overtake another vehicle before slowing down to travel at the same steady speed again.

3 Sketch a graph to show the depth of water in a bath where it is filled initially with just hot water, then the cold water is also turned on. After 2 minutes, a child gets into the bath, splashes about for 5 minutes before getting out, pulling the plug out with them. It takes 6 minutes for the water to drain away.

Answers

1 **a**   **b**   **c**   2 **a**   **b**   **c**

3 The graph may look something like this:

Framework objectives – Limits of sequences

Represent problems and synthesise information in algebraic form.

Oral and mental starter

- Ask: 'Who can multiply 15 by 13 mentally?' (195)
- Should anyone be able to do this, ask them to explain how they arrived at the answer. If a different method from what will be used in the lesson is used, use that as an alternative method.
- If no one is able to do this mentally, or as an alternative from the explanation offered, explain that you can split the sum into two parts.
- As $5 \times 3 = 15$, you can split the multiplication when multiplying by 15.
- For example, if you want to find 15×13, you can multiply 13 by 3 to get 39 and then multiply 39 by 5.
- There are various ways to multiply 39 by 5. One way is to multiply 39 by 10 and then halve the result. The number needed is half of 390. Halve this in two parts: half of 300 + half of 90 = 150 + 45 = 195.
- Ask the class to practise multiplying 16, 21, 34, 42 and 57 by 15. The table below can be used to check the results.

Number	16	21	34	42	57
Number × 15	240	315	510	630	855

Main lesson activity

- Put on the board: 'Divide by 5 and add 4.'
- Tell the class that this is a rule for creating a sequence and that this is the term-to-term rule.
- Ask someone to give you a number between 0 and 100. Use this to start the sequence. If you wish to have more control over the numbers, then choose your own starting number, say 1.
- Using the term-to-term rule, this will generate:
     1, 4.2, 4.84, 4.968, 4.9936, 4.99872, 4.999744, 4.999949
- Ask the class: 'Do you notice anything about the numbers?' They should notice that the terms are getting closer and closer to 5.
- The class will need calculators to do this, or could use a spreadsheet if available. If using a spreadsheet, they will need to know how to set up a formula and be able to copy it from one cell to another.

- **The class can now do Exercise 1E from Pupil Book 2.**

Exercise 1E Answers

1 a 1, 3.5, 4.75, 5.375, 5.6875, 5.84375, 5.921875, 5.9609375, 5.98046875, 5.990234375, 5.995117188, 5.997558594
  b 6   **c** The sequence always gets closer and closer to 6
2 a 1, 4.5, 6.25, 7.125, 7.5625, 7.78125, …
  b 8   **c** The sequence always gets closer and closer to 8
3 a 1, 5.5, 7.75, 8.875, 9.4375, 9.71875, 9.859375, …
  b 10   **c** The sequence always gets closer and closer to 10
4 a 12
5 Gets closer to 4.5
6 Gets closer to 6
7 Gets closer to 7.5
8 Gets closer to 9

1 3, 1200, Maria, 6, Kay, $1\frac{1}{2}$

2 a

Pattern number	Number of grey tiles	Number of white tiles
5	6	10
16	17	32

b

Pattern number	Expression for the number of grey tiles	Expression for the number of white tiles
n	$n + 1$	$2n$

c $3n + 1$ **d** $5n + 4$

3 a $\dfrac{n}{(2n + 1)}$ **b** $\frac{2}{5}, \frac{3}{10}, \frac{4}{17}$

The sequence always gets closer to $\dfrac{AB}{(A - 1)}$.

Plenary

Key Words

☐ **sequence**
☐ **term-to-term**

- Put on the board the term-to term rule 'divide by 2 and add 10'.
- Ask: 'Can anyone suggest what value this sequence will get closer and closer to? Why do you think that?'
- Students should be using the results from Questions 1 to 4 to help see a simple link, and that this sequence will get closer to 20.
- Now change the term-to-term rule to 'divide by 3 and add 10' and ask the same question.
- Using their results from Questions 5 to 8, the class may need help to see the link to multiplying the two numbers and halving the result to get the answer they require. Here, this gives the result of 15.

Homework

1 A sequence starting at 1 has the term-to-term rule *add three and divide by 2*.

  a Find the first 10 terms generated by this sequence.

  b To what value does this sequence get closer and closer?

  c Use the same term-to-term rule with different starting numbers. What do you notice?

2 Repeat Question 1, but change the term-to-term rule to *add 4 and divide by 2*.

3 What would you expect the sequence to do if you used the term-to-term rule *add 7 and divide by 2*?

4 What will the sequence get closer to using the term-to-term rule *add A and divide by 2*?

5 Investigate the term-to-term rule *add A and divide by 3*.

Answers
  1 b 3   **c** Always gets closer to 3
  2 b 4   **c** Always gets closer to 4
  3 Always gets closer to 7
  4 A
  5 The terms in the sequence will get closer to $\dfrac{A}{2}$.

Number 1

Framework objectives – Adding and subtracting fractions
Use efficient methods to add and subtract fractions.

Oral and mental starter

- Use a target board such as the one shown on the right.
- Start by asking the students, as a group or individually, to give the first five multiples of various numbers.
- Once the idea of the multiple is well established, ask for the **lowest common multiple (LCM)** of a pair of numbers. (It may be necessary to remind students of the definition.)
- Continue for as long as necessary.

2	5	7	8
24	15	18	3
6	9	27	14
12	20	10	25

Main lesson activity

- This is essentially a lesson on adding and subtracting fractions with different denominators.
- The students will have met this before, so they just need reminding of the basic rules and to have some more advanced techniques outlined.
- Ask them how to work out $\frac{5}{6} + \frac{3}{4}$.
- Recall the method of finding the LCM (12) and converting the original fractions to equivalent fractions as shown below.

$$\frac{5}{6} + \frac{3}{4} = \frac{10}{12} + \frac{9}{12}$$
$$= \frac{19}{12} = 1\frac{7}{12}$$

- The methods for converting between mixed numbers and improper (top-heavy) fractions may need to be revised.
- Repeat with $2\frac{5}{9} + 3\frac{7}{15}$.
- Outline the two methods for solving this addition. First, change to improper (top-heavy) fractions and proceed as above:

$$2\frac{5}{9} + 3\frac{7}{15} = \frac{23}{9} + \frac{52}{15}$$
$$= \frac{115}{45} + \frac{156}{45} = \frac{271}{45} = 6\frac{1}{45}$$

- Second, separate the whole numbers from the fractions:

$$2\frac{5}{9} + 3\frac{7}{15} = 2 + 3 + \frac{5}{9} + \frac{7}{15}$$
$$= 5 + \frac{25}{45} + \frac{21}{45}$$
$$= 5 + \frac{46}{45}$$
$$= 5 + 1\frac{1}{45} = 6\frac{1}{45}$$

- Discuss the comparative advantages and disadvantages of each method. For example, the first method involves larger numbers.
- Now ask the students how to work out $2\frac{5}{6} - 1\frac{2}{5}$.
- Show them both methods.

$$2\frac{5}{6} - 1\frac{2}{5} = \frac{17}{6} - \frac{7}{5}$$
$$= \frac{85}{30} - \frac{42}{30} = \frac{43}{30} = 1\frac{13}{30}$$
$$2\frac{5}{6} - 1\frac{2}{5} = 2 - 1 + \frac{5}{6} - \frac{2}{5}$$
$$= 1 + \frac{25}{30} - \frac{12}{30}$$
$$= 1 + \frac{13}{30} = 1\frac{13}{30}$$

- Ensure that the students understand the fact that the whole numbers are subtracted, the result of which is added to the result of subtracting the fractions.
- Repeat with $3\frac{1}{4} - 1\frac{9}{14}$, but use only the second method:

$$3\frac{1}{4} - 1\frac{9}{14} = 3 - 1 + \frac{1}{4} - \frac{9}{14}$$
$$= 2 + \frac{7}{28} - \frac{18}{28}$$
$$= 2 - \frac{11}{28}$$
$$= 1 + 1 - \frac{11}{28} = 1\frac{17}{28}$$

- Make sure that students know how to deal with the negative fraction.
- **The class can now do Exercise 2A from Pupil Book 2.**

Exercise 2A Answers

1 **a** $2\frac{11}{12}$ **b** $4\frac{17}{30}$ **c** $3\frac{11}{15}$ **d** $3\frac{5}{6}$ **e** $5\frac{19}{20}$ **f** $7\frac{1}{3}$ **g** $8\frac{17}{18}$ **h** $11\frac{1}{24}$
2 **a** $2\frac{1}{12}$ **b** $3\frac{7}{30}$ **c** $1\frac{1}{15}$ **d** $2\frac{1}{6}$ **e** $1\frac{13}{20}$ **f** $3\frac{2}{3}$ **g** $4\frac{17}{18}$ **h** $2\frac{23}{24}$
3 **a** 28 **b** 63 **c** 84 **d** 72
4 **a** $1\frac{11}{28}$ **b** $\frac{26}{63}$ **c** $\frac{9}{28}$ **d** $1\frac{13}{72}$
5 $22\frac{7}{9}$ cm
6 $6\frac{11}{12}$ cm
7 **a** $\frac{37}{80}$ **b** $\frac{13}{20}$ **c** $\frac{17}{96}$ **d** $\frac{22}{75}$

Extension Answers

Magic number is 1

$\frac{2}{15}$	$\frac{3}{5}$	$\frac{4}{15}$
$\frac{7}{15}$	$\frac{1}{3}$	$\frac{1}{5}$
$\frac{2}{5}$	$\frac{1}{15}$	$\frac{8}{15}$

Plenary

- On the board write a problem such as $2\frac{1}{12} + 3\frac{5}{8} - 1\frac{7}{18}$.
- Discuss the best way to solve such a problem.
- Work through using whichever method is thought to be appropriate.
- The separation method gives:
  $$2 + 3 - 1 + \frac{1}{12} + \frac{5}{8} - \frac{7}{18}$$
  $$= 4 + \frac{6}{72} + \frac{45}{72} - \frac{28}{72}$$
  $$= 4 + \frac{23}{72} = 4\frac{23}{72}$$

Key Words

- [ ] **convert**
- [ ] **equivalent fraction**
- [ ] **mixed number**
- [ ] **top-heavy fraction**
- [ ] **improper fraction**
- [ ] **lowest common multiple**

Homework

Convert each of the following pairs of fractions to equivalent fractions with a common denominator. Then work out each answer, cancelling down and/or writing as a mixed number if appropriate.

a $2\frac{2}{5} + 2\frac{1}{4}$ **b** $2\frac{2}{3} + 1\frac{1}{8}$ **c** $2\frac{2}{3} + 1\frac{5}{7}$ **d** $2\frac{1}{5} + 3\frac{7}{8}$

e $2\frac{2}{5} - 1\frac{1}{4}$ **f** $2\frac{1}{3} - 1\frac{5}{6}$ **g** $2\frac{5}{8} - 1\frac{5}{12}$ **h** $3\frac{5}{12} - 1\frac{3}{4}$

Answers
a $4\frac{13}{20}$ **b** $3\frac{19}{24}$ **c** $4\frac{8}{21}$ **d** $6\frac{3}{40}$ **e** $1\frac{3}{20}$ **f** $\frac{1}{2}$ **g** $1\frac{5}{24}$ **h** $1\frac{2}{3}$

LESSON 2.2

Framework objectives – Multiplying and dividing fractions

Use efficient methods to multiply and divide fractions, interpreting division as a multiplicative inverse. Cancel common factors before multiplying or dividing.

Oral and mental starter

- Using a target board such as the one shown on the right, pick individual students and ask each one to cancel a fraction to its simplest terms.

$\frac{5}{10}$	$\frac{8}{10}$	$\frac{8}{16}$	$\frac{4}{16}$	$\frac{4}{12}$
$\frac{6}{12}$	$\frac{6}{10}$	$\frac{24}{10}$	$\frac{24}{12}$	$\frac{14}{12}$
$\frac{14}{21}$	$\frac{7}{21}$	$\frac{7}{14}$	$\frac{12}{14}$	$\frac{12}{15}$
$\frac{5}{15}$	$\frac{5}{25}$	$\frac{20}{25}$	$\frac{20}{16}$	$\frac{14}{16}$

Main lesson activity

- This is the first time that the students will have met multiplication and division of fractions.
- One way to introduce this topic is to use calculators to investigate the answers to products such as $\frac{1}{5} \times \frac{3}{5}$, $\frac{5}{7} \times \frac{1}{4}$ and $\frac{3}{4} \times \frac{3}{8}$. The students will see the rule very quickly.
- Now repeat with $\frac{1}{2} \times \frac{4}{5}$, $\frac{3}{4} \times \frac{8}{9}$ and $\frac{4}{15} \times \frac{3}{8}$. Ask why the rule doesn't appear to work. Discuss cancelling in the initial product and in the answer.
- Explain that it is better to cancel the initial fractions, as this makes the calculations easier and means that the answer does not need to be cancelled down. Demonstrate with

$$\frac{\cancel{4}^{1}}{\cancel{9}_{3}} \times \frac{\cancel{25}^{5}}{\cancel{28}_{7}} \times \frac{\cancel{3}^{1}}{\cancel{10}_{2}} = \frac{5}{42}$$

- Now ask for the answer to $2\frac{1}{5} \times 1\frac{7}{8}$. Explain how this is done, namely:

$$2\frac{1}{5} \times 1\frac{7}{8} = \frac{11}{\cancel{5}_{1}} \times \frac{\cancel{15}^{3}}{8} = \frac{33}{8} = 4\frac{1}{8}$$

- Make sure that the students know that the mixed numbers cannot be separated as in addition or subtraction. They must be converted to improper (top-heavy) fractions.
- Division is a little harder to see. If calculators are used, investigate problems such as $\frac{2}{7} \div \frac{1}{3}$, $\frac{3}{4} \div \frac{4}{5}$ and $\frac{2}{3} \div \frac{8}{9}$, some students may see the method.
- They are unlikely to see that it is the same as turning the dividing fraction upside down and multiplying by it. Demonstrate this with the above examples.
- This is an easy method to use but not an easy one to understand. It can best be explained by examples such as how many halves in 7? The answer is, of course, the same as multiplying by 2.
- Now ask for the answer to $2\frac{2}{3} \div 1\frac{5}{9}$. Explain how this is done, namely:

$$2\frac{2}{3} \div 1\frac{5}{9} = \frac{8}{3} \div \frac{14}{9} = \frac{\cancel{8}^{4}}{\cancel{3}_{1}} \times \frac{\cancel{9}^{3}}{\cancel{14}_{7}} = \frac{12}{7} = 1\frac{5}{7}$$

- Do more examples if necessary.
- **The class can now do Exercise 2B from Pupil Book 2.**

Plenary

- Write the following problem on the board: $4\frac{1}{5} \div 10\frac{1}{2} \times \frac{3}{8}$.
- Work through it, cancelling whenever possible. The answer is $\frac{3}{20}$.
- Repeat for $1\frac{1}{8} \times 4\frac{1}{3} \times \frac{2}{13}$ (answer: $\frac{3}{4}$) and $(\frac{3}{8} + \frac{5}{6}) \div (\frac{3}{4} + \frac{1}{18})$ (answer: $1\frac{1}{2}$).

Key Words

- [ ] **cancelling**
- [ ] **mixed number**
- [ ] **improper fraction**
- [ ] **top-heavy fraction**

Homework

1 Work out each of the following. Cancel before multiplying when possible.

    a $\frac{1}{6} \times \frac{3}{8}$ b $\frac{2}{3} \times \frac{3}{4}$ c $\frac{2}{9} \times \frac{3}{16}$ d $4\frac{1}{5} \times 1\frac{3}{7}$ e $2\frac{3}{8} \times 1\frac{3}{5}$

2 Work out each of the following. Cancel at the multiplication stage when possible.

    a $\frac{1}{4} \div \frac{1}{3}$ b $\frac{3}{16} \div \frac{9}{14}$ c $\frac{1}{6} \div \frac{1}{3}$ d $2\frac{5}{8} \div \frac{7}{16}$ e $2\frac{3}{5} \div \frac{3}{10}$

Answers
1 a $\frac{1}{16}$ b $\frac{1}{2}$ c $\frac{1}{24}$ d 6 e $3\frac{4}{5}$
2 a $\frac{3}{4}$ b $\frac{7}{24}$ c $\frac{1}{2}$ d 6 e $8\frac{2}{3}$

Framework objectives – Percentages and compound interest
Recognise when fractions or percentages are needed to compare proportions.
Solve problems involving percentage changes.

Oral and mental starter

- Use a target board such as the one shown on the right.
- Ask the students for the equivalent multiplier when there is a percentage increase or decrease. For example, 1.05 is the multiplier for a 5% increase and 0.95 for a 5% decrease.
- Go round the class picking students at random and asking for the appropriate multipliers for an increase and/or a decrease for percentages on the board.

5%	10%	22%	13%
16%	25%	14%	35%
20%	17%	6%	15%
8%	12%	$7\frac{1}{2}$%	2%

Main lesson activity

- This is a lesson on **compound interest**. Start by asking the students what they know about interest and how it works.
- Emphasise the basis of compound interest, namely: an amount of money (the principal) is invested at an annual percentage rate (R%), and over a period of years the value increases by R% each year,
- Make sure that the students understand that the interest for each year is added to the principal of the previous year to give the new principal for the following year.
- Work through an example. First, use the method of working out the yearly interest and adding it on for each year; then use a multiplier. For example, calculate how much £300 will earn when invested for 3 years at 4% interest per annum.

First method   *Increase and add on*
After first year: 4% of £300 = £12. So, at end of first year, you have £300 + £12 = £312
After second year: 4% of £312 = £12.48. So, at end of second year, you have £312 + £12.48 = £324.48
After third year: 4% of £324.48 = £12.98. So, at end of third year, you have £324.48 + £12.98 = £337.46

Second method   *Use a multiplier*
After first year: £300 × 1.04 = £312
After second year: £312 × 1.04 = £324.48
After third year: £324.48 × 1.04 = £337.46

- Point out that the last value is rounded to the nearest penny.
- Most students are likely to prefer the second method. However, some will prefer the structured nature of the first method.
- Demonstrate the use of powers on a calculator. For example, the above result is identical to $300 \times (1.04)^3$. This gives 337.4592, which has to be rounded to the nearest penny.
- Discuss the advantage (quick) and the disadvantage (any keying errors mean no working from which to gain partial credit).
- Repeat with an example that decreases each year. For example, an ant colony has 30 000 ants. They start to die off at the rate of 22% per day. How many ants will be left after 7 days?
- The first method is too lengthy. The second method (using the multiplier of 0.78) gives:
  30 000, 23 400, 18 252, 14 236.56, 11 104.52, 8661.52, 6755.99, 5269.67
  Hence, there are 5270 ants left at the end of 7 days.

- **The class can now do Exercise 2C From Pupil Book 2.**

1 **a** 1.12 **b** 0.95 **c** 0.92 **d** 1.07 **e** 0.96 **f** 1.02 **g** 1.032 **h** 1.025
  i 0.85 **j** 1.06 **k** 0.974 **l** 1.005 **m** 0.76 **n** 0.93 **o** 1.175
2 **a** £216.49 **b** £3740.06 **c** £214.90 **d** £19 348.42 **e** £80.77
3 **a** £2348.27 **b** £219.15 **c** £1334.49
4 **a** 33 662 **b** 18 837
5 6 days
6 12 days

a £547.50 **b** £47.54 **c** £47.30
d £47.07, £46.83, £46.60, £46.37, £46.14, £45.91, £45.68, £45.45, £45.23, £45
e £555.12

Plenary

Key Words

☐ **compound**
☐ **interest**
☐ **multiplier**

- Discuss the advantages/disadvantages of using a multiplier and powers compared with other methods.
- If the class is able enough, establish the formula for compound interest:

$$\text{Total at end of period} = \text{Initial amount} \times \left(1 \pm \frac{\text{Percentage rate}}{100}\right)^{\text{Time period}}$$

So, take as an example 45 000 units decreasing at 6% each day for 3 days, which gives:

$$\text{Total after 3 days} = 45\,000 \times \left(1 - \frac{6}{100}\right)^3 = 37\,376.28 \text{ units}$$

Homework

1 How much would you have in the bank if you invest as follows?

  a £450 at 3% interest per annum for 4 years

  b £6000 at 4.5% interest per annum for 7 years

2 Stocks and shares can decrease in value as well as increase. How much would your stocks and shares be worth if you had invested as follows?

  a £1000, which lost 14% each year for 3 years

  b £750, which lost 5.2% each year for 5 years

Answers
  1 a £506.48 **b** £8165.17
  2 a £636.06 **b** £574.25

Framework objectives – Reverse percentages and percentage change

Use proportional reasoning to solve a problem, choosing the correct numbers to take as 100%, or as a whole.

Oral and mental starter

- Use a target board such as the one shown on the right.
- Ask the students for the equivalent percentage increase or decrease for each multiplier. For example, 1.05 represents a 5% increase.
- Go round the class picking students at random and asking for the appropriate percentage increase and/or decrease for the multipliers on the board.

1.05	0.90	1.22	0.87	0.6
1.16	0.75	1.14	1.35	1.3
0.8	0.81	1.06	0.65	0.02
0.92	1.12	1.175	0.98	1.88

Main lesson activity

- This lesson is about **reverse percentages** and how to choose the appropriate quantity to take as 100%.
- Ask the students for the original amount when the new value, after a 30% increase, is £195.
- Many may suggest that it is the same as a 30% decrease of £195, which is £136.50. When the latter amount is increased by 30%, the answer is £177.45.
- Explain that £195 represents not 100% but 130%.
- Solve the problem using first the unitary method, and then a multiplier.

> **Method 1** *Unitary method*
> This involves finding a single unit value, which in this case is the value of 1%.
> £195 represents 130%
> £1.50 represents 1%   (dividing both sides by 130)
> £150 represents 100%   (multiplying both sides by 100)

> **Method 2** *Use a multiplier*
> A 30% increase is represented by the multiplier 1.30.
> Hence, divide £195 by 1.3 to find the original amount. This gives:
> $195 \div 1.3 = £150$

- Discuss the disadvantages/advantages of each method. The students will probably prefer to use the multiplier, as it is easier to work out and has fewer steps.
- Repeat with other examples if necessary.
- Now ask the students: 'What is the percentage increase from £550 to £704?'
- Do the calculation on the board:
  Actual increase = £704 – £550 = £154
  $$\text{Percentage increase} = \frac{£154}{£550} \times 100 = 28\%$$
- Emphasise that £550 is the original amount.

- **The class can now do Exercise 2D from Pupil Book 2.**

Plenary

- Introduce the 'magic road sign', which is a mnemonic to help to recall the different combinations used in the calculation of percentage change and reverse percentages.

That is:

New value = Original value × Multiplier
Multiplier = New value ÷ Original value
Original value = New value ÷ Multiplier

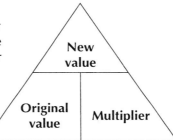

Key Words

- reverse
- percentage
- unitary method
- multiplier
- power

Homework

1. A packet of biscuits claims to be 24% bigger! It now contains 26 biscuits. How many did it have before the increase?

2. After a 10% price decrease, a hi-fi system now costs £288. How much was it before the decrease?

3. This table shows the cost of some items after $17\frac{1}{2}$% VAT has been added. Work out the cost of each item before VAT.

Item	Cost inc VAT	Item	Cost inc VAT
Radio	£112.80	Cooker	£329
Table	£131.60	Bed	£376

4. A pair of designer jeans is on sale at £96, which is 60% of its original price. What was the original price?

5. A pair of boots, originally priced at £60, were reduced to £36 in a sale. What was the percentage reduction in the price of the boots?

Answers
1. 21 biscuits
2. £320
3. radio £96, table £112, cooker £280, bed £320
4. £160
5. 40%

Framework objectives – Ratio

Compare two ratios.

Interpret and use ratio in a range of contexts, including solving word problems.

Oral and mental starter

- Practice is given here in mentally dividing a two-digit by a single-digit number.
- Explain the method of dividing a carry remainder with the next digit. For example, if doing $78 \div 3$ (=26), the mental picture should be as shown on right.
- Ask the students individually, or as a group (answers could be written on white boards), the following: $72 \div 4$ (=18), $85 \div 5$ (=17), $96 \div 3$ (=32), $84 \div 6$ (14), $92 \div 4$ (=23).

Main lesson activity

- This lesson is a revision of ratio, which has not been met in relation to Number since Year 7.
- Start by reminding the students of how to apply the rules of ratio.
- Ratios compare quantities and are usually written in their simplest form. Normally, ratios need to be in the same units.
- Ratios can be cancelled to give their simplest form. For example, 4 : 10 can be cancelled by 2 to yield 2 : 5. Here, the link to cancelling fractions should be mentioned. Do some examples of cancelling, such as 10 : 25 (= 2 : 5), 8 : 18 (= 4 : 9), 15 : 21 (= 5 : 7).
- Now explain that when we want to compare quantities using ratios, they must be either in the form $1 : m$ or $n : 1$.
- In the case of $1 : m$, explain that the method is to divide both values in the ratio by the first value. Give as an example a comparison of the areas of two photographs, A and B. A has an area of 125 cm² and B an area of 300 cm². Hence, we have:

  A : B
  125 : 300
    1 : 2.4   (Divide through by 125)

  which gives:

  Area of B = 2.4 × Area of A
- If necessary, repeat with other examples.
- In the same way, we can write ratios in the form $n : 1$ by dividing through by the second value. Give as an example a comparison of the length of the body of an actual racing car with that of a model of the car. The actual car has a body length of 3.77 metres, and the model a length of 26 cm. Hence, we have:

  Actual Car : Model
       377 : 26   (Change to a common unit, cm)
      14.5 : 1   (Divide through by 26)

  which gives:

  Length of actual car = 14.5 × Length of model
- Now recall the method for dividing a quantity in a given ratio. For example, divide £550 in the ratio 5 : 6.

  The ratio 5 : 6 means that the quantity is first divided into 5 + 6 = 11 equal parts. That is, 11 parts = £550, giving one part is £550 ÷ 11 = £50. Hence, 5 parts = 5 × 50 = £250, and 6 parts = 6 × £50 = £300.
- Point out that the total of the final quantities should equal the starting value.
- **The class can now do Exercise 2E from Pupil Book 2.**

Exercise 2E Answers

1 **a** $1:3$ **b** $5:8$ **c** $4:9$ **d** $3:5$ **e** $5:8$ **f** $1:3$ **g** $3:10$ **h** $1:3$
   i $2:5:7$ **j** $2:3:5$
2 **a** $1:4$ **b** $1:3.2$ **c** $1:2.5$ **d** $1:2.5$ **e** $1:8$ **f** $1:3.5$ **g** $1:3.33$ **h** $1:3$
   i $1:3$ **j** $1:1.5$
3 **a** $1.33:1$ **b** $0.625:1$ **c** $0.4:1$ **d** $0.36:1$ **e** $0.3125:1$ **f** $0.25:1$
   g $0.3:1$ **h** $0.33:1$ **i** $0.4:1$ **j** $0.6:1$
4 $1:1.5625$, $1:1.6$; first alloy has greater proportion of gold
5 $1.875:1$, $1.857:1$; second class has greater proportion As
6 **a** £120 : £200 **b** £45 : £165 **c** £500 : £300 **d** £306 : £144
7 300 g
8 14 kg
9 875 ml
10 **a** 4:7 **b** Weight not needed as the ratio is $100:175$

Extension Answers

a **i** $1:2$ **ii** $1:4$ **iii** $1:8$
b **i** $1:6$ **ii** $1:36$ **iii** $1:216$
c **i** $1:3$ **ii** $1:9$ **iii** $1:27$
Area ratios are the squares of the length ratios and the volume ratios are the cubes of
them.

Plenary

Key Words

- ☐ ratio
- ☐ simplest form
- ☐ proportion

- Ask the students how to use ratio to solve the following problem.
  A large jar of jam costs 87p for 500 g and a small jar costs 28p for 150 g.
  Which is the better value?
  > Putting the values as ratios gives $87:500$ and $28:150$.
  > In the form $1:n$, these are $1:5.75$ and $1:5.36$, which represent the
  > number of grams per penny.
  > In the form $n:1$, these are $0.174:1$ and $0.187:1$, which represent the
  > number of pence per gram.
  > Both of these sets of ratios show that the large jar is the better value.

Homework

1 Cancel each of the following ratios to its simplest form.

   a $9:21$ **b** $10:45$ **c** $18:24$ **d** $12:15$

2 Write each of the following ratios in the form $1:n$.

   a $10:9$ **b** $20:7$ **c** $8:12$ **d** $30:50$

3 Write each of the following ratios in the form $n:1$

   a $12:25$ **b** $26:50$ **c** $20:4$ **d** $15:8$

4 **a** Divide £480 in the ratio $3:5$ **b** Divide £240 in the ratio $1:1.5$

Answers
1 **a** $3:7$ **b** $2:9$ **c** $3:4$ **d** $4:5$
2 **a** $1:0.9$ **b** $1:0.35$ **c** $1:1.5$ **d** $1:1.67$
3 **a** $0.48:1$ **b** $0.52:1$ **c** $5:1$ **d** $1.875:5$
4 **a** £180 : £300 **b** £96 : £144

LESSON 2.6

Framework objectives – Numbers between 0 and 1

Understand the effects of multiplying and dividing by numbers between 0 and 1.
Use the laws of arithmetic and inverse operations.

Oral and mental starter

- This brief starter could be missed out.
- Quickly recall the rules for multiplying and dividing with directed numbers. Do this with a few examples, such as:

$$-2 \times +3 = -6 \qquad -4 \div -1 = +4 \qquad -5 \div 0.5 = -10$$

Main lesson activity

- This lesson is essentially an investigation. The class can work in groups or individually. Keep the introduction as brief as possible.
- The introduction and Example 2.14 from Pupil Book 2 are reproduced here.

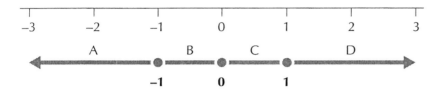

The special numbers –1, 0 and 1 divide the number line into four sets of numbers: A, B, C and D.
A contains all the numbers less than –1. B contains all the numbers between –1 and 0. C contains all the numbers between 0 and 1 and D contains all the numbers greater than 1.

Example 2.14
  a What happens when a number from set A is multiplied by a number from set D?
  b What happens when a number from set B is divided by 1?

  a Choose any number from set A, say –2. Choose any number from set D, say +3. Multiply them together:

$$-2 \times +3 = -6.$$

The answer belongs to set A.

Try other combinations of numbers from set A and set D. For example:

$$-4 \times +4 = -16 \qquad -1.5 \times 5 = -7.5 \qquad -5 \times 1.5 = -7.5$$

They all belong to set A. So, a number from set A multiplied by a number from set D always gives a number in set A.

  b Pick numbers from set B and divide each one by 1. For example:

$$-0.4 \div 1 = -0.4 \qquad -\tfrac{2}{3} \div 1 = -\tfrac{2}{3} \qquad -0.03 \div 1 = -0.03$$

The answers are the same as the values from set B. So, they all give numbers in set B.

- This example, or similar examples, could be worked through to start the investigation.

- **The class can now do Exercise 2F from Pupil Book 2.**

Exercise 2F Answers

1

×	A	–1	B	0	C	1	D
A	D	D	C/D	0	A/B	A	A
–1	D	1	C	0	B	–1	A
B	C/D	C	C	0	B	B	A/B
0	0	0	0	0	0	0	0
C	A/B	B	B	0	C	C	C/D
1	A	–1	B	0	C	1	D
D	A	A	A/B	0	C/D	D	D

2

÷	A	–1	B	0	C	1	D
A	C/D	D	D		A	A	A/B
–1	C	1	D		A	–1	B
B	C	C	C/D		A/B	B	B
0	0	0	0		0	0	0
C	B	B	A/B		C/D	C	C
1	B	–1	A		D	1	C
D	A/B	A	A		D	D	C/D

3 a ii **b** iv **c** iii **d** ii

4 For example: **a** $-8 \div -1 = 8$ **b** $7 \times -0.2 = -1.4$ **c** $9 \div -0.2 = -45$
d $-6 \times -0.5 = +3$

Extension Answers

No firm conclusions can be reached. The results depend on the numbers chosen.

Plenary

- The answers to the two tables (Exercise 2F, Questions 1 and 2) should be discussed with the whole class. Highlight particularly the significance of multiplying and dividing by numbers between 0 and 1.
- Familiarise them with the term **counter-example**.

Homework

1 Say which of these statements is true. If it is not true, give a counter-example.

a The square of a number between 0 and 1 is also between 0 and 1.

b The square of a number between 0 and –1 is also between 0 and –1.

c Dividing any number by a number between 0 and 1 always gives a bigger answer.

d Dividing any positive number by a number between 0 and 1 always gives a bigger answer.

Answers
1 a True **b** False, for example: $(-0.4)^2 = 0.16$ **c** False, for example: $-7 \div 0.5 = -14$, which is smaller
d True

Framework objectives – BODMAS
Understand the order of precedence and effect of powers.

Oral and mental starter

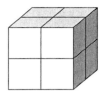

- As preparation for the mental test in the SATs papers, this starter concentrates on SATs style questions using powers. Ask each question twice and allow about 10 seconds for the students to answer.
  1 What is nine squared?
  2 What is the square root of 144?
  3 The diagram shows a cube made from smaller cubes. [Draw this on the board.] What is the volume of the big cube?
  4 The length of one side of a square is 4 cm. What is the area of the square?
  5 The area of a square is 64 cm². What is the perimeter of the square?
  6 x squared is 4. Which two values can x have?
  7 Look at the inequality. [Write $x^2 < 17$ on the board.] What is the largest integer value that x could be?
  8 What number is five cubed?
  9 The nth term of a sequence is n plus one all squared. [Write $(n + 1)^2$ on the board.] What is the fifth term of the sequence?
  10 What is the square root of nine-sixteenths?
- It might be worthwhile discussing the techniques involved when giving the answers.
- It is useful to repeat this test within a few days to see whether scores improve.

  Answers **1** 81 **2** 12 **3** 8 (cm³) **4** 16 cm² **5** 32 cm **6** 2 and –2
  7 4 **8** 125 **9** 36 **10** Three-quarters

Main lesson activity

- This is a revision lesson on BODMAS, concentrating especially on powers.
- Remind the students of the order of precedence.
- Work through some examples, such as that given below.

$64 \div (3^2 + 7) - 5 + 2(6 - 3)^2$
$= 64 \div (9 + 7) - 5 + 2 \times 3^2$ Work on the brackets first, starting on the left with the power in the bracket.
$= 64 \div 16 - 5 + 2 \times 3^2$ Evaluate the first bracket.
$= 64 \div 16 - 5 + 2 \times 9$ Work out the remaining power.
$= 4 - 5 + 2 \times 9$ Divide.
$= 4 - 5 + 18$ Multiply.
$= 17$

- When addition and subtraction are the only operations, work from left to right. Similarly, when the only operations are multiplication and division, work from left to right. Work through the three examples below.

○ $(3 + 2)^2 \times (3^2 + 4)$ $= 5^2 \times (9 + 4)$ Evaluate the left bracket and the power in the right bracket.
    $= 5^2 \times 13$ Resolve the bracket.
    $= 25 \times 13$ Evaluate the power.
    $= 325$

○ $[3 + (4^2 - 1) \div 5] + 3$ $= [3 + (16 - 1) \div 5] + 3$ With nested brackets, first calculate the inside bracket.
    $= [3 + 15 \div 5] + 3$ Divide and resolve the
    $= 3 + 3 + 3$ remaining bracket.
    $= 9$

$$\circ \quad \frac{(3 \times 4)^2}{6 \times 2} = \frac{\overset{1}{\cancel{3}} \times \overset{2}{\cancel{4}}{}^{1} \times 3 \times 4}{{}_{1}\underset{1}{\cancel{2}}\cancel{6} \times \cancel{2}{}_{1}}$$

$$= 12$$

Note It is sometimes beneficial to write out the expression in full, so that the numbers can be cancelled easily.

- **The class can now do Exercise 2G from Pupil Book 2.**

Exercise 2G Answers

1 **a** 50   **b** 5   **c** 2   **d** 4.5   **e** 0.625   **f** 1.8   **g** 120   **h** 9   **i** 3
2 **a** 36   **b** 95   **c** 2.5   **d** 10
3 **a** $(5 - 1)^2 \times 4 - 2 = 62$ **b** $5 - (1^2 \times 4) - 2 = -1$ **c** $(5 - 1)^2 \times (4 - 2) = 32$
   d $(3 + 2)^2 + 4 \times 2 = 33$ **e** $3 + (2^2 + 4) \times 2 = 19$ **f** $(3 + 2^2 + 4) \times 2 = 22$
4 **a** 0.6   **b** 3   **c** 4   **d** 2700
5 **a** 12   **b** 84   **c** 9   **d** 1.96   **e** –31   **f** –121   **g** 41   **h** 19

Extension Answers

a Subtract 8, divide by 5, $x = 2$ **b** Multiply by 6, add 3, $x = 57$ **c** Divide by 3, add 7, $x = 10$ **d** Add 2, multiply by 3, $x = 36$

Plenary

- Put a long BODMAS problem on the board and ask the students to evaluate it step by step. This could be done either a line at a time by individual students, or as a class activity. Here is an example:

$$[(3 + (2 + 1)^2) \div (6 - 2)^2] \times [(5 - 3)^2 \div 3] \quad \text{(Answer: 1)}$$

Key Words

- order of operations
- bracket
- power
- nested brackets

Homework

Use BODMAS to evaluate each of these.

a $(3 + 4)^2 \times (6 - 3)$ **b** $(5^2 - 4) \div (2 + 1)^2$ **c** $(4 + 4^2) \div (2 \div 2)^3$

d $48 \div (9 - 1) - 8 + 2(18 \div 6)^3$ **e** $(5 + 2) \times 3^2 - 5(2^3 - 4)$

f $[7 + (4 - 1)^2] \div 3(4 - 2)^2$ **g** $(5 - 2)^3 \div [(4 - 1) + (3^2 - 3)]$

h $\dfrac{5 \times 4^2}{10 \times 2}$ **i** $\dfrac{(5 \times 4)^2}{10 \times 2}$

Answers
a 147   **b** 2.33   **c** 20   **d** 52   **e** 43   **f** 1.33   **g** 3   **h** 4   **i** 20

Framework objectives – Rounding and approximation

Make and justify estimates and approximations of calculations.

Oral and mental starter

- Have a set of Follow-me cards dealing with approximations. A set of 20 are given below. These should be given to pairs of students to allow discussion. It is suggested that each pair be given a few moments to come up with an estimate (the teacher can write each one on the board) and that jottings are allowed.

  1 START. You are 0.52×0.62
  2 I am approx. 0.3. You are 892×0.48.
  3 I am approx. 450. You are 0.29×0.31
  4 I am approx. 0.09. You are 58×72.
  5 I am approx. 4200. You are 0.32×61
  6 I am approx. 18. You are 312×0.32.
  7 I am approx. 90. You are 217×53
  8 I am approx. 10 000. You are 0.092×0.12
  9 I am approx. 0.009. You are 6.2×0.72
  10 I am approx. 4.2. You are 187×0.68.
  11 I am approx. 140. You are 3.2×0.33
  12 I am approx. 0.9. You are 39×51.
  13 I am approx. 2000. You are $(72)^2$
  14 I am approx. 4900. You are 0.32×0.11
  15 I am approx. 0.03. You are 504×189
  16 I am approx. 100 000. You are 96×0.11.
  17 I am approx. 10. You are $(0.68)^2$
  18 I am approx. 0.49. You are 92×89.
  19 I am approx. 8100. You are 0.092×321
  20 I am approx. 27. END.

Main lesson activity

- This is a lesson on making approximations.
- Ask the students to round the following numbers as indicated: 368 to the nearest 100, 23.9 to the nearest 10, 0.0713 to one decimal place.
- Ask them whether the answers have anything in common.
- They may notice – or may need to be prompted to state – that the answers all have one digit apart from zero.
- These are examples of rounding to one significant figure (1 sf).
- This is a concept that many students find hard to grasp. Emphasise that there will be only one digit apart from any zeros.
- Do more examples of rounding to one significant figure, such as:
  $$3789 \approx 4000 \qquad 0.265 \approx 0.3 \qquad 25 \approx 30 \qquad 198 \approx 200 \qquad 636 \approx 600$$
  $$0.0621 \approx 0.06 \qquad 0.0764 \approx 0.08$$
- Now give some examples of how rounding to 1 sf can be used to estimate answers to calculations. For example:
  $$320 \times 398 \approx 300 \times 400 = 120\,000$$
  $$0.092 \times 476 \approx 0.09 \times 500 = 0.9 \times 50 = 9 \times 5 = 45$$
  $$(29 + 88) \div (2.3 \times 5.3) \approx (30 + 90) \div (2 \times 5) = 120 \div 10 = 12$$
  $$17 \div 0.42 \approx 20 \div 0.4 = 200 \div 4 = 50$$
- Do more examples if necessary.

- **The class can now do Exercise 2H from Pupil Book 2.**

1   **a** 600   **b** 300   **c** 7000   **d** 100   **e** 30   **f** 0.09   **g** 300   **h** 0.4   **i** 0.7
    j 6000   **k** 900   **l** 100
2   **a** 80 000   **b** 1 500 000   **c** 4200   **d** 160 000   **e** 8100   **f** 0.18   **g** 0.063
    h 0.04   **i** 100   **j** 140   **k** 240   **l** 420
3   **a** 6   **b** 30   **c** 5   **d** 400   **e** 40   **f** 50   **g** 500   **h** 600   **i** 400   **j** 50   **k** 400
    l 0.3
4   **a** $0.7 \times 600 = 420$ **b** $300 \div 50 = 6$ **c** $3000 \div 0.6 = 5000$
    d $0.06 \times 0.2 = 0.012$ **e** $(20 \times 5) + 600 = 700$ **f** $(4 + 6) \times (7 + 8) = 150$
    g $(200 \times 10) \times (800 \div 2) = 2000 \times 400 = 800 000$ **h** $5 \times (3 - 0.4) = 5 \times 2.6 = 13$
    i $5^2 \times 8 \div 0.2^2 = 25 \times 8 \div 0.04 = 200 \div 0.04 = 5000$
    j $(20 \times 4) \div (2 + 0.5) = 80 \div 2.5 = 32$

Extension Answers

a 350   **b** 4220   **c** 4200   **d** 0.619   **e** 0.62   **f** 300   **g** 4700   **h** 4700
i 0.079   **j** 978.3   **k** 978   **l** 980

SATs Answers

1   **a** 600 ml   **b** 50 ml   **c** No, 1 : 4 is 20%
2   £2.12   £12.25
3   **a** 14.5%   **b** 17 255   **c** 39.3%
    d Not enough information: total number of police officers not given for both years.
4   **a** 48%   **b** 1 : 5.8   **c** $\frac{15}{34}$
5   **a** 70×1.09; 70×0.9 is 90% of 70, 70×1.9 is 70 increased by 90%, 70×0.09 is
    9% of 70   **b** 0.86
6   For example: Let $t = 1$, $w = 1$. Then $\dfrac{1}{1} + \dfrac{1}{1} = 1 + 1 = 2$ but $\dfrac{2}{1 + 1} = \dfrac{2}{2} = 1$, and $2 \neq 1$

Plenary

- Put the following on the board:
    $(14.7 \times 3.9) \div (0.96 + 0.59)$
- Ask a student to round to 1 sf and approximate the answer. That is:
    $(10 \times 4) \div (1 + 0.6) = 40 \div 1.6$
- At this stage, the problem becomes too difficult to do mentally.
- Ask whether it is possible to approximate differently. For example:
    $(15 \times 4) \div (1 + 0.5) = 60 \div 1.5 = 40$
- Point out that approximations do not have to be made to 1 sf when a more sensible approximation is possible.
- Try this out with $23.6 \times 7.8 \div 49.2$. Rounding to 1 sf gives $20 \times 8 \div 50$, but rounding to $25 \times 8 \div 50 = 4$ is easier to do mentally.

Key Words
- most significant digit
- least significant digit
- approximate
- significant figure

Homework

1   By rounding each value to one significant figure, estimate the answer to each of the following.
    a 0.83×793 **b** $618 \div 32$ **c** $812 \div 0.38$
    d 0.78×0.049 **e** $(38 \times 3.2) - 48.7$ **f** $(2.7 + 6.3) \times (5.2 - 1.7)$

Homework answers
1   **a** $0.8 \times 800 = 640$ **b** $600 \div 30 = 20$ **c** $800 \div 0.4 = 2000$ **d** $0.8 \times 0.05 = 0.04$ **e** $(40 \times 3) - 50 = 70$
    f $(3 + 6) \times (5 - 2) = 27$

Algebra 3

Framework objectives – Equations and formulae

Distinguish the different roles played by letter symbols in equations and formulae.

Oral and mental starter

- Ask the class for the largest multiple of 9 less than 100 (it is 99).
- Repeat this for the largest multiples less than 100 of these numbers:
  7 (98); 8 (96); 13 (91); 3 (99)
- Discuss how people found the answers. It would probably be by adding on from known facts or by trial and error. Working from known facts is a good way to find the answer.
- Now ask for the largest multiple of 7 under 300. Demonstrate the following method for finding it.
  Start from $300 \div 7$ which can be seen to be about 40.
  Calculate $7 \times 40 = 280$, add on sevens to get 287 then 294, which is the largest multiple (as only 6 less than 300).
- Now ask individual students to find each of the following using a similar method.
  Largest multiple of 6 less than 500 (498)
  Largest multiple of 7 less than 400 (399)
  Largest multiple of 8 less than 300 (296)
  Largest multiple of 11 less than 700 (693)
  Largest multiple of 15 less than 800 (795)

Main lesson activity

- Write an equation on the board such as $7x + 3 = 17$
- Ask the class what this is – you want the response 'equation'.
- Discuss the fact that x represents a specific value, and that to solve the equation is to find the value for x that makes the equation correct.
- Ask if anyone can tell you what to do to try and solve this equation.
- You want the response 'subtract 3 from both sides', which gives $7x + 3 - 3 = 17 - 3$
- This simplifies to $7x = 14$
- Ask what we should do next. If someone simply gives the correct final solution of 2, ask them what it was they did in their heads that allowed them to get to this answer.
- You want the response 'divide both sides by 7', giving the solution $x = 2$.
- They may have simply arrived at this answer 'by inspection' – that is, by using their knowledge of the 7-times table. Establish that this is equivalent to the method of dividing through.
- You will need to go through some different types of linear equations to ensure the class are very familiar with what they should be doing to solve equations. Use some examples such as those below.
  $4(2x - 3) = 44$ ($x = 7$; start by dividing through by 4)
  $2(3x + 1) = 4(x + 3)$ ($x = 5$; start by expanding the brackets)
- **The class can now do Exercise 3A from Pupil Book 2.**

Plenary

- Talk about formulae and equations, bringing out the fact that a formula is used to find various values given some others, whereas an equation is written with just one unknown value. Solving an equation means finding the solution to it.

Key Words
- equation
- solve
- solution

Homework

1 Solve the following equations.

   a $5(x + 7) = 45$ **b** $3(x - 5) = 12$ **c** $6(y + 3) = 48$ **d** $5(m - 7) = 55$

2 Solve the following equations.

   a $6(x - 5) = 4(x + 2)$ **b** $4(x - 1) = 2(x + 3)$ **c** $6(x + 3) = 4(x + 5)$

3 Solve the following equations.

   a $5(m - 2) - 4(m + 3) = 0$ **b** $5(k + 4) - 3(k - 6) = 0$

   c $4(y + 7) - 3(y + 5) = 0$ **d** $3(2x - 4) - 2(4x + 5) = 0$

4 Identify whether each of the following is an equation or a formula.

   i $4x + 7 = 3x - 7$ **ii** $y = 4y + 3$ **iii** $t = 8 + 9t$

   iv $W = 5q - R$ **v** $p = 4m + 8n$ **vi** $w + 7 = 3w - 1$

Answers
   1 **a** 2   **b** 9   **c** 5   **d** 18
   2 **a** 19   **b** 5   **c** 1
   3 **a** 22   **b** –19   **c** –13   **d** –11
   4 **i** equation   **ii** equation   **iii** equation   **iv** formula   **v** formula   **vi** equation

Framework objectives – Solving problems using equations
Construct and solve linear equations with integer coefficients.

Oral and mental starter

- Tell the class that they will be playing the 'guess my number' game. Tell them that all the numbers will be positive, whole numbers, less than 100.
- Think of a number, say 61, write it on a piece of paper and put it somewhere obvious but unseen, such as on top of the board. Challenge the class to guess this number by asking questions which require a 'yes' or 'no' answer. Can they do it in fewer than 10 questions?
  Possible questions are: 'is it even?'; 'is it a multiple of 5?'; 'is it less than 50?', etc.
- Keep a check on the number of questions they are asking and help them to avoid unnecessary questions, such as asking if it is even, when it is already known to be not odd.
- Some variations on this activity are: teacher asking the class the questions; two teams versus each other; teams of two, each playing another pair. The advantage of the latter is that all the students will be engaged in the activity.

Main lesson activity

- Introduce the problem:
  'I am thinking of a number. If I multiply it by 4, then subtract 5, then divide it by 3, I get the final answer 13. What is my number?'
- Discuss the strategy the pupils are using to suggest answers, which could vary from trial and error to working backwards from 13.
- Explain to the pupils that this is a situation where algebra is particularly useful.
- Start with letting the unknown number be x (or any other letter the class may want to suggest).
- Then go through the problem – multiply it by 4 [to give $4x$], then subtract 5 [$4x - 5$], then divide by 3 $\left[\dfrac{(4x - 5)}{3}\right]$, giving us the result 13.
- This sets up the equation $\dfrac{(4x - 5)}{3} = 13$ and we can set about solving it.

$$\frac{(4x - 5)}{3} = 13 \qquad \text{multiply both sides by 3}$$
$$4x - 5 = 39 \qquad \text{add 5 to both sides}$$
$$4x = 44 \qquad \text{divide both sides by 4}$$
$$x = 11$$

- Demonstrate that this is the solution by substituting 11 into the original word problem.
- Now give the class another problem:
  'Three friends have 200 cards between them. Joe has 36 more cards than Chris, Kay has twice as many cards as Chris. How many cards does each friend have?'
- Set up the problem by choosing a value to be represented by a letter. A sensible choice here is to let x be the number of cards that Chris has.
- This means Joe has $x + 36$ and Kay has $2x$ cards.
- As the total number of cards is 200, we can now write the equation:
  $$x + (x + 36) + 2x = 200$$
- Work through simplifying then solving this to give $x = 41$.
- So Chris has 41 cards, Joe has 77 cards and Kay has 82 cards.

- **The class can now do Exercise 3B from Pupil Book 2.**

1 11
2 48
3 I sheared 8 sheep, my brother 38 sheep and Uncle Ned sheared 159 sheep.
4 Joy had 9, Amy had 23 and Nicola had 32
5 72 cm^2
6 6
7 Catherine is 27, her mother 56
8 James now has 52 and Helen has 104
9 Brian spent E154 and Gillian spent E462
10 26
11 52
12 42 minutes
13 Lisa 240, Kathryn 480 and Sally 390

Extension Answers

1 Monday 114, Tuesday 104, Wednesday 154, Thursday 116, Friday 104, Saturday 208
2 A = 100°, B = 50°, C = 30°

Plenary

Key Words

☐ **variable**
☐ **equation**
☐ **solution**

● Ask the students why it is that we were able to solve each of the problems in the Pupil Book exercise by algebra.
● The answer is because in each case we can express each value in the problem in terms of one variable, because we are told how they are all related.
● If this is not true of a problem, then it may not be possible to solve it using algebra.
● You may need to go through one or two of the problems in the exercises to illustrate what it means to express all the values in terms of a single variable.

Homework

1 I think of a number, add 5, divide by 3 then add 11. The final answer is 17. What was the number I was thinking of?

2 I double my son's age, divide by 3, then add 2. I end up with the age of my daughter who is 20. How old is my son?

3 The length of a rectangle is three times its width. Its perimeter is 56 cm. What is the area of the rectangle?

4 Wesley and Beverly had 223 DVDs between them. For Beverley's birthday, Wesley bought her a box set of 5 DVDs, which meant that she now has half as many as Wesley. How many DVDs does Wesley have?

Answers
1 13
2 27
3 147 cm^2
4 152

Oral and mental starter

- Ask for some equivalent fractions to $\frac{1}{2}$. After a few correct suggestions of $\frac{2}{4}$, $\frac{5}{10}$, etc., ask for an equivalent fraction to $\frac{1}{2}$ that uses the number 34.
- The two possible answers are $\frac{34}{68}$ and $\frac{17}{34}$.
- Now ask for two fractions equivalent to $\frac{1}{3}$ that use the number 12 ($\frac{12}{36}$ and $\frac{4}{12}$).
- Repeat this with the following examples:

  equivalent to $\frac{1}{5}$ using the number 45   ($\frac{45}{225}$ and $\frac{9}{45}$)

  equivalent to $\frac{2}{3}$ using the number 18   ($\frac{18}{27}$ and $\frac{12}{18}$)

  equivalent to $\frac{1}{4}$ using the number 28   ($\frac{28}{112}$ and $\frac{7}{28}$)

  equivalent to $\frac{3}{4}$ using the number 36   ($\frac{36}{48}$ and $\frac{27}{36}$)

Main lesson activity

- Put on the board the equation $\frac{x}{3} = 5$ and ask the class how we solve it.
- You should be given the response 'multiply both sides by 3', which gives $x = 15$.
- Explain that is a simple equation using fractions, but they did meet a more difficult one last lesson, something like

  $$\frac{(4x + 5)}{3} = 7$$

- Ask 'how do we solve this?'
- Again it's a matter of simplifying the side around the variable (x) step-by-step.
- Start by multiplying both sides by 3 to give $4x + 5 = 21$, then subtract 5 from both sides to give $4x = 16$, then divide both sides by 4 to give $x = 4$.
- Tell the class they will meet a slightly more complex sort today. Write the following example on the board:

  $$\frac{x - 1}{2} = \frac{2x + 8}{6}$$

- Explain that when there is a fraction on both sides like this, the first step is to find the product of the denominators and multiply by it. Here $2 \times 6 = 12$, so we multiply both sides by 12 to give:

  $$\frac{12 \times (x - 1)}{2} = \frac{12 \times (2x + 8)}{6}$$

- Now remind the students about cancelling fractions, as we now need to see that the denominator on each side will cancel with the 12 to give $6(x - 1) = 2(2x + 8)$.
- Expand each side to give $6x - 6 = 4x + 16$, show how we add six to each side, then subtract $4x$ from each side to give $2x = 22$ and $x = 11$.
- **At this stage let the class do Questions 1 to 4 from Exercise 3C from Pupil Book 2.**
- When they have shown some understanding of this process, you may want to show them a more difficult problem, such as:

  $$\frac{4(2x + 1)}{5} = \frac{2(2x - 4)}{3}$$

- Again multiply both sides by the product of the denominators and then cancel down, giving:

  $$\frac{15 \times 4(2x + 1)}{5} = \frac{15 \times 2(2x - 4)}{3}$$

  which cancels down to $12(2x + 1) = 10(2x - 4)$.
- Expanding and simplifying gives the solution $x = -13$.

- **The class can now complete Exercise 3C from Pupil Book 2.**

Plenary

● Put on the board the equation $\dfrac{12}{x} = 2$ and ask the class if anyone can solve the problem.

● They should see that the solution is $x = 6$, but discuss with the class the methods that they might have used in order to get that solution if it had been a much harder problem.

● Give them the problem $\dfrac{245}{x} = 14$ and ask how this could be solved.

● Multiply both sides by x to give $245 = 14x$, then divide both sides by 14 to give $x = 17.5$.

Homework

1 Solve the following equations.

a $\dfrac{x}{7} = 4$ **b** $\dfrac{t}{6} = 2$ **c** $\dfrac{m}{9} = 5$ **d** $\dfrac{x}{3} = 8$ **e** $\dfrac{w}{7} = 8$

2 Solve the following equations.

a $\dfrac{3x}{5} = 12$ **b** $\dfrac{3t}{5} = 6$ **c** $\dfrac{6m}{8} = 18$ **d** $\dfrac{2x}{5} = 8$ **e** $\dfrac{2w}{7} = 6$

3 Solve the following equations.

a $\dfrac{x + 1}{3} = 5$ **b** $\dfrac{x + 5}{4} = 8$ **c** $\dfrac{2x + 4}{5} = 6$ **d** $\dfrac{3x + 1}{8} = 2$

4 Solve the following equations.

a $\dfrac{x - 1}{3} = \dfrac{x + 1}{4}$ **b** $\dfrac{2x + 3}{3} = \dfrac{x - 2}{2}$ **c** $\dfrac{3x - 2}{5} = \dfrac{x + 4}{2}$

LESSON 3.4

Framework objectives – Equations involving x^2

Solve equations involving positive and negative solutions using appropriate methods.

Oral and mental starter

- Ask 'what is the largest number that goes into both 12 and 18?'
- You should receive the correct answer of 6 after a few attempts. Remind the class that we call this the highest common factor or HCF.
- Ask what the HCF is of 200 and 300 (100).
- Discuss with the class how they could have seen this fairly easily, as 100 is an obvious, large factor of both numbers.
- Ask what the HCF is of 60 and 90 (30).
- Discuss with the class what they need to do to find this. Encourage the method of looking for factors of the smaller number from halfway, getting smaller. Here this would give 30 straightaway, as half of 60.
- Explain why we do not need to look at any numbers greater than half of the smaller number (unless the smaller number is itself a factor of the larger one).
- Ask what the HCF is of 75 and 165 (15).
- Again discuss the strategy used, once the number has been found.
- Ask what the HCF is of 60 and 80 (20)

Main lesson activity

- Draw a square on the board and tell the class that its area is 25 square centimetres. What are the lengths of its sides?
- This should provoke some discussion and the answer should come readily as 5 cm.
- Then put on the board the equation $x^2 = 49$ and say that this equation could represent a similar problem. Explain that this could be about a square with area 49 cm² and side of length x. Solving the equation to find x will tell us the length of the side.
- Ask for the value of x. Establish that $x = 7$ (the square root of 49), so the square has a side of length 7 cm.
- Now ask 'is 7 the only possible solution to this equation?' This should provoke discussion, with some suggestions of other numbers, which must be shown to be wrong. Lead the pupils into negative numbers and the fact that a possible solution is $x = -7$. Point out that although this is not a sensible answer for the length of the side of the square, it is perfectly acceptable as an alternative solution to the equation.
- Put on the board the equation $x^2 = 81$ and ask for the solution. We need the positive and negative square roots of 81, which are $x = 9$ and $x = -9$
- Now increase the difficulty slightly by putting on the board the equation $x^2 + 13 = 29$
- Ask the pupils what we can do to solve this. You should get the response 'subtract 13 from each side to give $x^2 = 16$, which gives the solutions $x = 4$ and $x = -4$'.
- Finish this session with the example $(x - 3)^2 = 36$ and ask for suggestions as to how we can solve it.
- You should get to $(x - 3) = 6$ and -6
  Hence $(x - 3) = 6$, which leads to $x = 9$, and $(x - 3) = -6$ which leads to $x = -3$
- **The class can now do Exercise 3D from Pupil Book 2.**

1 **a** $x = 5$ and -5 **b** $x = 9$ and -9 **c** $m = 7$ and -7 **d** $t = 1.2$ and -1.2
  e $t = 20$ and -20
2 **a** $x = 6$ and -6 **b** $x = 5$ and -5 **c** $m = 7$ and -7 **d** $t = 9$ and -9
  e $t = 4$ and -4 **f** $x = 8$ and -8 **g** $k = 12$ and -12 **h** $g = 11$ and -11
  i $h = 7$ and -7 **j** $t = 7$ and -7 **k** $n = 8$ and -8 **l** $y = 9$ and -9
3 **a** $x = 1$ and -7 **b** $x = 3$ and -13 **c** $m = 6$ and -8 **d** $t = 23$ and -37
  e $t = 15$ and -25 **f** $k = 4$ and -20 **g** $x = 5$ and -1 **h** $h = 10$ and -2
  i $n = 18$ and -4
4 **a** $x = 5$ and -5 **b** $x = 6$ and -6 **c** $x = 4$ and -4 **d** $x = 8$ and -8
  e $x = 7$ and -7 **f** $x = 9$ and -9
5 7 or -7
6 18 or -8
7 178 or 222
8 28 and -4

1 **a** 175 **b** 518 and 598
2 **a** $x = 3$ and -5 **b** $m = 2$ and -8 **c** $x = 8$ and -12 **d** $k = 4$ and -10
  e $n = 18$ and -10 **f** $y = 20$ and -10

Plenary

Key Words

- Ask for the solutions to $x^2 = 100$
- These are $x = 10$ and $x = -10$
- Now ask if anyone can suggest the solution to $x^2 = 289$
- We want the square root of 289, does anyone know it? (There may be someone, congratulate them if they get it right as 17.)
- Otherwise we might want to use a calculator, this will tell us that the square root is 17, but we need to remember to put in the negative solution too.
- Set the class some more examples, such as: $x^2 = 1156$ (solution $x = 34$ and -34) and $x^2 = $ one million (solution $x = 1000$ and -1000).

☐ **square root**

Homework

1 Solve these equations. Each has two solutions.

  a $x^2 + 7 = 32$ **b** $x^2 + 18 = 34$ **c** $m^2 + 34 = 83$

2 Solve these equations. Each has two solutions.

  a $(x + 6)^2 = 121$ **b** $(x - 5)^2 = 16$ **c** $(m - 1)^2 = 49$

3 Solve these equations. Each has two solutions.

  a $6 = \dfrac{216}{x^2}$ **b** $5 = \dfrac{245}{x^2}$ **c** $8 = \dfrac{648}{x^2}$

4 I square a number, add 48 to it and get 112. What are the two possible numbers I could have squared?

5 I think of a number, subtract 7, square it and get the answer 289. What are the two possible numbers I could be thinking of?

Answers
1 **a** $x = 5$ and -5 **b** $x = 4$ and -4 **c** $m = 7$ and -7
2 **a** $x = 5$ and -17 **b** $x = 9$ and 1 **c** $x = 8$ and -6
3 **a** $x = 6$ and -6 **b** $x = 7$ and -7 **c** $x = 9$ and -9
4 8 or -8
5 24 or -10

LESSON 3.5

Framework objectives – Trial and improvement

The systematic trial and improvement method to find approximate solutions to equations such as $x^3 + x = 20$

Oral and mental starter

- Ask the class if anyone can tell you the solution to $x^2 = 45$
- It should quickly become clear that since 45 is not a square number, only an approximate answer can be given.
- We are looking for the two whole numbers between which the solution lies. These will be 6 and 7, as $6^2 = 36$ and $7^2 = 49$. The solution looks closer to 7 than 6, so we might estimate this as 6.7 (and –6.7).
- Repeat this process for the following numbers:
    $x^2 = 58$, between 7 and 8, estimate 7.6
    $x^2 = 158$, between 12 and 13, estimate 12.6
    $x^2 = 179$, between 13 and 14, estimate 13.4

Main lesson activity

- Tell the students that some equations are quite difficult to solve and we have to use different techniques to solve them. Write on the board $x^2 + x = 23$ and ask how we might find a solution to one decimal place.
- After some discussion and suggestions, which may well include trial and improvement, tell the students you are going to show them a logical and efficient way to pursue this solution by trial and improvement (ensure they realise that this is *not* trial and error).
- Tell them that first, we need to find two consecutive integers between which the solution lies.
- At this point start the table of attempts, as shown on the right.
- Establish that the consecutive integers are 4 and 5.
- Once we know the solution lies between 4 and 5, narrow the search by trying the number halfway between, that is 4.5. Use a calculator for these calculations.
- The range is now between 4 and 4.5. We sense that perhaps the solution is closer to 4.5, hence try 4.25, but rounded up to 4.3
- The range is now 4.3 to 4.5, so we can try halfway here, which is 4.4
- So we now have two consecutive, one decimal place numbers 4.3 and 4.4
- To one decimal place, the solution is one of these, but we cannot just take the one that gives the closest answer to 23. In order to be sure, we have to narrow the range again by trying the halfway number of 4.35
- This shows us the answer lies between 4.3 and 4.35. Hence the solution to $x^2 + x = 23$ to one decimal place is $x = 4.3$

x	$x^2 + x$	Comment
4	20	too small
5	30	too big
4.5	24.75	too big
4.3	22.79	too small
4.4	23.76	too big
4.35	23.27	too big

- Now write the equation $x^3 - x = 43$. You may want to let the students try to find the answer by trial and improvement themselves (to 1 dp.). Make sure they all start off with the correct integers, as shown in the table, then check their progress every now and again. Individual students may well take a slightly different route where the halfway number is not at an exact value, but do encourage intelligent thinking while doing that.
- The table on the right gives one possible route to the solution of $x = 3.6$ to 1dp.

- **The class can now do Exercise 13E from Pupil Book 2.**

x	$x^3 - x$	Comment
3	24	too small
4	60	too large
3.5	39.375	too small
3.7	46.95	too large
3.6	43.06	too large
3.55	41.19	too small

36

Plenary

- Ask the students what they think will be the largest number of guesses that they should need to guess an integer between 0 and 100 (if they are told 'larger' or 'smaller' for each guess).
- Show that they should never need more than 7 guesses if they use the logical way of narrowing down the range by halving each time.
- Ask how many this will be if the number is now a one decimal place value between 0 and 100 (this time 10).

Homework

Find, to one decimal place, the solution to each of the following equations. Use a trial and improvement method in each case.

a $x^2 + x = 65$ **b** $x^2 - x = 99$ **c** $x^3 + x = 100$ **d** $x^3 - x = 50$

Answers
  a 7.6 **b** 10.5 **c** 4.6 **d** 3.8

Framework objectives – Graphs showing direct proportion

Solve problems involving direct proportion, relating algebraic solutions to graphical implementation.

Oral and mental starter

- Tell the class that you were looking at a DVD yesterday and noted that the running time was 135 minutes. Ask the class how many hours and minutes this is (2 hours 15 minutes).
- Discuss with the class how they calculate this, using multiples of 60 to find the number of hours with the remainder being minutes.
- Now ask 'What fraction of an hour is 15 minutes?' Ask for both a fraction and a decimal answer ($\frac{1}{4}$ and 0.25).
- Now ask 'What fraction of an hour is 10 minutes?' This is $\frac{1}{6}$ as a fraction, but the decimal is more awkward. Can the class determine what the decimal answer would be without using a calculator?
- Starting from known facts, $\frac{1}{3} = 0.3333333$ and $\frac{1}{6}$ is half of this, so $\frac{1}{6} = 0.1666667$, by short division.
  Alternatively, $\frac{3}{6} = \frac{1}{2} = 0.5$, and $\frac{4}{6} = \frac{2}{3} = 0.6666667$, so $\frac{1}{6} = \frac{4}{6} - \frac{3}{6} = 0.6666667 - 0.5 = 0.1666667$
- Now ask 'What fraction of an hour is 5 minutes?'. This is $\frac{1}{12}$, which is half of $\frac{1}{6}$ or 0.083333
- Talk about the potential confusion of using decimal notation in time; that is, 1.50 could mean $1\frac{1}{2}$ hours or 1 hour 50 minutes. The students should be sure they know which unit is being used.

Main lesson activity

- Tell the class that you took a taxi journey late at night and watched the taxi fare change on the display. The table shows the fares at various times after getting into the taxi.

Time	00:15	00:20	00:30	00:35
Fare (£)	1.30	3.00	6.40	8.10

- Draw a pair of axes with time on the x-axis and label them. Mark the x-axis with one hour as the principal unit, subdivided into 5-minute sections. Ensure there is enough room to extend the y-axis down to at least –4. Now plot the points and draw a suitable straight line through them.
- Explain to the pupils that as the line is straight, you can say that the two variables have a linear relationship. Furthermore the fare increase in a time interval is **directly proportional** to the length of time. This means that the fare always increases by the same amount for a given increase in time. You can show that this works out as £1.70 every 5 minutes.
- Ask the students what the equation of the line will be in terms of time, t, in hours, and fare, f, in pounds.
- Remind the pupils of the general equation of a straight line: $y = mx + c$, where m is the gradient and c is the y-axis intercept.
- In one hour, the fare would have increased by 12 × £1.70 which is £20.40, so the gradient is 20.4
- Extend the vertical axis down to –4, then demonstrate that the line cuts it at $f = -3.8$
- Therefore the equation of the line is $f = 20.4t - 3.8$
- Explain that the extra points we are using to find the equation of the line are impossible points for real life, since you can't have a negative fare, but they are useful to help us find the relationship.
- Ask what the fare would be at 00:50 if the same rate continued.

- You can use the graph, or use the equation, but if you use the equation then you must change 50 minutes into hours ($\frac{50}{60}$ = 0.833 hours) so giving £13.20
- **The class can now do Exercise 3F from Pupil Book 2.**

Exercise 3F Answers

1 **b** yes   **c** $C = 1.5t - 8$ **d** 16°C
2 **b** yes   **c** $f = 48\,000t - 58\,000$ **d** between 12 and 13 minutes past 1
3 **b** yes   **c** $L = \dfrac{w}{100} + 10$ **d** 1700 g
4 **b** yes   **c** $S = 52t - 156$ **d** 338
5 **b** approximately, yes   **c** B = approximately $0.66H$ **d** approximately 760 cm

SATs Answers

1 **a** $4n + 5$ **b** $3n + 4$ **c** 105
2 $y = 7.3$
3 **a** 2   **b** 1   **c** $\frac{7}{3}$ **d** 2
4 **a** $(1 \times 1) + (2 \times n) + (3 \times 5) + (4 \times 6) + (5 \times 3) = 55 + 2n$ **b** $15 + n$ **c** 10

Extension Answers

a Approximately 10.40 AM   **b** 5 times

Plenary

- Ask the pupils what is meant by 'directly proportional'.
- They need an understanding that this means that one variable always increases by the same amount for a given increase in the other variable. The graph of two variables that are directly proportional will always be linear (that is, a straight line) and pass through the origin.
- Discuss the fact that it wasn't always easy to find the equation of the lines in the Pupil Book exercise. Using the idea of $y = mx + c$ will always help them in this respect.

Key Words

- directly proportional
- linear relationship

Homework

A baby squid is weighed from birth at midday for its first 5 days. The results are shown in the table below.

Day	1	2	3	4	5
Weight (kg)	1.7	3.1	4.5	5.9	7.3

a Plot the points on a graph and join them with a suitable line.

b Is the increase in weight during a time interval directly proportional to the length of the interval?

c Write down the equation of the line showing the relationship between the weight (W) and the age (D) of the squid.

d If the relationship held, at what age would the squid first weigh over 15 kg?

Answers
   b yes   **c** $W = 1.4D + 0.3$ **d** Day 11

Shape, Space and Measures 1

Framework objectives – Angles of polygons

Explain how to find, calculate and use the sums of the interior and exterior angles of quadrilaterals, pentagons and hexagons.

Solve problems using properties of angles, of parallel and intersecting lines, and of triangles and other polygons, justifying inferences and explaining reasoning with diagrams and text.

Oral and mental starter

- Tell the students to imagine an equilateral triangle ABC.
- Now tell them to imagine that the base line AB is fixed and the vertex C is allowed to move parallel to the base.
- Next, ask the students to describe what other types of triangle can be formed as C moves.

  Answers Scalene triangles, two right-angled triangles and two isosceles triangles.

Main lesson activity

- Remind the class that the sum of the interior angles of a triangle is 180°, and that the sum of the interior angles of a quadrilateral is 360°. Illustrate by splitting a quadrilateral into two triangles.
- Ask the class to write down the names of all the other **polygons** that they met in Year 7: pentagon, hexagon, heptagon, octagon, nonagon, decagon.
- Make sure that the students understand the definition of a **regular polygon**.
- Show the class how to find the sum of the **interior angles** of a hexagon. Show how a hexagon can be split into four triangles from one of its vertices.
- The sum of the interior angles for each triangle is 180°. So, the sum of the interior angles of a hexagon is $4 \times 180° = 720°$.
- Explain to the class how to form an **exterior angle** of a polygon by extending a side of a polygon. In the diagram, a is an exterior angle of the quadrilateral.
- Show the class how to extend the sides to give all the exterior angles of a pentagon.
- Standing on a **vertex** and turning through all the exterior angles on the pentagon, you will have turned through 360°. Explain that this is true for all polygons.
- The students can write in their books: For any polygon, the sum of the exterior angles is 360°.
- Ensure that the class understands that, at any vertex of a polygon, the interior angle plus the exterior angle = 180° (angles on a straight line). In the diagram, $b + c = 180$.
- **The class can now do Exercise 4A from Pupil Book 2.**

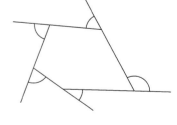

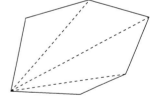

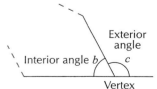

Interior angle b / c

Exterior angle

Vertex

Exercise 4A Answers

1 a (i) 720° **(ii)** 1080°

b

Name of polygon	Number of sides	Number of triangles inside polygon	Sum of interior angles
Triangle	3	1	180°
Quadrilateral	4	2	360°
Pentagon	5	3	540°
Hexagon	6	4	720°
Heptagon	7	5	900°
Octagon	8	6	1080°
n-sided polygon	n	$n - 2$	$180(n - 2)°$

2 a 100° **b** 150° **c** 285° **3 a** 80° **b** 110° **c** 52° **4** 120°
5 140°, 110°, 40°, 70°
6 a a = 50° (angles on a line), b = 130° (angles on a line), c = 50° (alternate angles), d = 130° (corresponding angles) **b** e = 70° (angles on a line), f = 110° (alternate angles), g = 120° (angles on a line), h = 60° (alternate angles)

Extension Answers

1 a 128° **b** 30° **c** 20° **d** 15° **e** 25°

Plenary

- Invite a student to go to the board to explain how to find the sum of the interior angles of a polygon.
- Ask another student to give the value of the sum of the exterior angles of a polygon.
- Invite a third student to explain, on the board, the connection between the interior angle and the exterior angle at any vertex of a polygon.

Key Words

- exterior angle
- interior angle
- polygon

Homework

1 Find the sum of the interior angles for each of the following polygons.

a Pentagon **b** Hexagon **c** Octagon

2 Calculate the unknown angle in each of the following polygons.

a

b

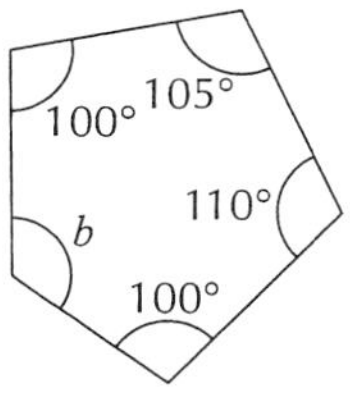

c

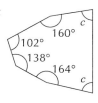

d

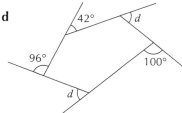

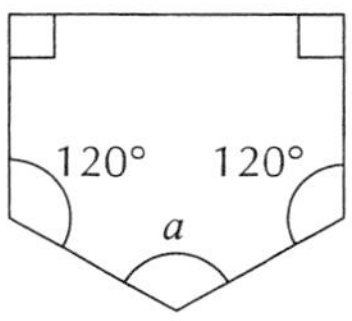

3 Calculate the value of x in each of the following polygons.

a

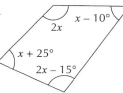

b

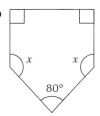

c

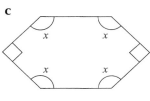

Answers
1 a 540° **b** 720° **c** 1080° **2 a** 120° **b** 125° **c** 78° **d** 61° **3 a** 60° **b** 140° **c** 135°

LESSON

4.2

Framework objectives – Angles of regular polygons

Explain how to find, calculate and use the interior and exterior angles of regular polygons.

Solve problems using properties of angles, triangles and other polygons, justifying inferences and explaining reasoning with diagrams and text.

Oral and mental starter

- Tell the students to imagine a square.
- Now tell them to imagine cutting the square along one of its diagonals.
- Next, ask the students to describe the two shapes that are left. Answer: two isosceles right-angled triangles.
- Then tell them to imagine cutting the square again, but this time along a line which is parallel to the diagonal.
- Finally, get the students to describe the two shapes that are left. Answer: an isosceles right-angled triangle and a pentagon.

Main lesson activity

- Remind the class of the definition of a regular polygon. A polygon is regular when all its interior angles are equal and all its sides have the same length.
- Explain that the lesson is about how to calculate the size of each exterior and interior angle of any regular polygon.
- Draw a regular pentagon on the board or OHP, with one of its exterior angles labelled x and the interior angle labelled y, as in the diagram below.
- The regular pentagon has five equal exterior angles, the sum of which is 360°. So, we have:

$$5x = 360°$$
$$x = 72°$$

- The regular pentagon also has five equal interior angles. The sum of an interior angle and exterior angle is 180°. So, we have:

$$y = 180° - 72° = 108°$$

- **The class can now do Exercise 4B in Pupil Book 2.**

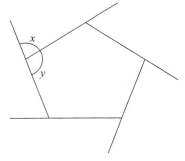

1

Regular polygon	Number of sides	Sum of exterior angles	Size of each exterior angle	Size of each interior angle
Equilateral triangle	3	360°	120°	60°
Square	4	360°	90°	90°
Regular pentagon	5	360°	72°	108°
Regular hexagon	6	360°	60°	120°
Regular octagon	8	360°	45°	135°
Regular decagon	10	360°	36°	144°
Regular n-sided polygon	n	360°	$\dfrac{360°}{n}$	$180° - \dfrac{360°}{n}$

2 a 30° **b** 150° **c** 1800°   **3 a** isosceles **b** 36° **c** 36°   **4** 36°
5 $a = 90°$, $b = 120°$, $c = 30°$
6 $\angle$AFB = $22\frac{1}{2}°$ **7** 18   **8** 20

1 a 51.4°, 128.6°   **b** 40°, 140°

Plenary

Key Words

- exterior angle
- interior angle
- regular polygon

- Conduct a quick revision test to ensure that the students can recall the size of the exterior and interior angles for common regular polygons.
- Ask the class to write down the size of each exterior angle and each interior angle for each of these shapes.
  1 Equilateral triangle **2** Square **3** Regular pentagon **4** Regular hexagon
       Answers 1 120°, 60° **2** 90°, 90° **3** 72°, 108° **4** 60°, 120°

Homework

1 Calculate the size of **i** each exterior angle and **ii** each interior angle for each of the following regular polygons.

   a Pentagon   **b** Hexagon   **c** Octagon

2 ABCDE is a regular pentagon. Calculate the size of the angle marked x on the diagram.

   Explain, with reasons, how you obtained your answer.

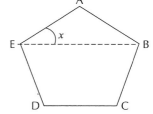

3 ABCDEFGH is a regular octagon. Calculate the size of the angle marked y on the diagram.

   Explain, with reasons, how you obtained your answer.

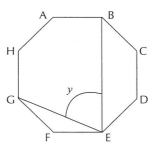

Answers
   1 a i 72° **ii** 108° **b i** 60° **ii** 120° **c i** 45° **ii** 135°
   2 $\angle$BAE = 108° (interior angle of regular pentagon), $\triangle$ABE is isosceles. So,
   $$x = \frac{180° - 108°}{2} = 36°$$
   3 $\angle$BEF = 90° (by symmetry), $\angle$EFG = 135° (interior angle of regular octagon),
   $\triangle$EFG is isosceles. So, $\angle$GEF = $\dfrac{180° - 135°}{2} = 22\frac{1}{2}°$, giving $y = 90° - 22\frac{1}{2}° = 67\frac{1}{2}°$

LESSON 4.3

Framework objectives – The circle and its parts

Know the definition of a circle and the names of its parts. Explain why inscribed regular polygons can be constructed by equal divisions of a circle.

Oral and mental starter

- Draw a circle and a vertical line on the board or OHP, as in the diagram.
- Tell the class to imagine the line getting closer to the circle, passing through the circle and then moving to the other side of the circle.
- Ask the class to draw on their white boards or on the board, the different situations which can occur.
- **Answer**

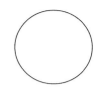

Touches at a point	Cuts the circle twice	Passes through the centre	Touches at a point again	Does not touch again

Main lesson activity

- Explain to the class that a circle is a set of points equidistant from a fixed point, called the **centre**, designated here by O.
- Describe the following terms for the class. They can copy the diagrams into their books, if required.

Circumference The length round a circle. It is a special name for the perimeter of a circle.

Arc One of the two parts between two points on a circumference.

Radius The distance from the centre of a circle to its circumference. The plural of the term is 'radii'.

Diameter The distance across a circle through its centre. The diameter d of a circle is twice its radius r so, $d = 2r$

Chord A straight line which joins two points on the circumference of a circle.

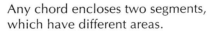

Tangent A straight line that touches a circle at one point only on the circumference. This point is called the **point of contact**.

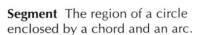

Segment The region of a circle enclosed by a chord and an arc.

Any chord encloses two segments, which have different areas.

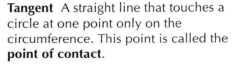

Sector A portion of a circle enclosed by two radii and one of the arcs between them.

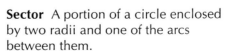

Semicircle One half of a circle: either of the parts cut off by a diameter.

- **The class can now do Exercise 4C from Pupil Book 2.**

Plenary

- The class will require two sets of prepared workcards. One set contains all the terms for the different parts of the circle. The other set contains the definitions.
- Tell the class to work in pairs or small groups.
- Both sets of cards should be placed face down on the table.
- Each student in each pair/group should turn over two of the cards. When two cards match, they are left face up. Otherwise, they are turned back, face down.
- The activity ends when all the cards have been turned over. The activity can then be repeated if time permits.

Key Words

- [ ] **arc**
- [ ] **centre**
- [ ] **chord**
- [ ] **circumference**
- [ ] **diameter**
- [ ] **radius**
- [ ] **sector**
- [ ] **segment**
- [ ] **tangent**
- [ ] **inscribed**

Homework

1 Draw each of the following circles.

  a Radius = 2 cm   b Radius = 3.5 cm   c Diameter = 5 cm   d Diameter = 6.4 cm

2 Draw each of the following diagrams accurately.

  a   b   c

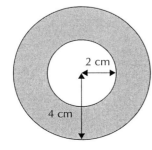

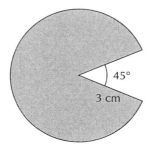

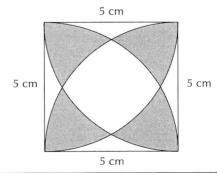

Framework objectives – Tessellations and regular polygons

Explain how to find, calculate and use the interior angles of regular polygons.

Solve problems using properties of angles, of parallel and intersecting lines, and of polygons, justifying inferences and explaining reasoning with diagrams and text.

Oral and mental starter

- Show the class two transparencies, each displaying a set of parallel lines 4 cm apart, as below.

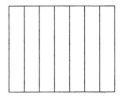 

- Ask them what shapes are formed when one transparency is placed on top of the other and one of them is rotated.
- Then show them that only squares and rhombuses can be formed.
- Now ask the class what shapes can be formed when one of the transparencies has parallel lines 2 cm apart. (Answer: rectangles and parallelograms)

Main lesson activity

- Remind the class about tessellations, which they met in Year 7. A tessellation is a pattern made on a plane (flat) surface with identical shapes which fit together exactly, leaving no gaps. Explain that it is usual to draw up to about ten of the shapes to show the tessellating pattern.
- Show the class how equilateral triangles and squares tessellate.
- Ask the class whether any other regular polygons will tessellate. Explain that they will be doing a practical activity to discover which of the regular polygons tessellate and the reason why.
- For Exercise 4D, the class will require squared paper, isometric paper, card for making regular polygon templates and scissors. Sets of commercially produced, regular polygons can also be useful, so that the students can easily visualise the shapes, particularly if they have difficulty in making their own templates.
- **The class can now do Exercise 4D from Pupil Book 2.**

2 b There are gaps **3 b** There are gaps (squares)

4 a

Regular polygon	Size of each interior angle	Does polygon tessellate?
Equilateral triangle	60°	Yes
Square	90°	Yes
Regular pentagon	108°	No
Regular hexagon	120°	Yes
Regular octagon	135°	No

b Size of the interior angle divides exactly into 360°
c No, each interior angle of a regular nonagon is 140°, which does not divide exactly into 360°

Plenary

- Invite a student to the board and give her/him a regular polygon, asking the student to show whether it tessellates.
- Continue to invite individual students to the board, giving each a different polygon.

Key Words

- interior angle
- regular polygon
- tessellate

Homework

1 Work out, by making templates or by drawing diagrams, which of the following regular polygons tessellate, and which do not. In each case, write down a reason for your answer.

   a Equilateral triangle **b** Square **c** Regular pentagon **d** Regular hexagon **e** Regular octagon

2 Draw a diagram to show how squares and equilateral triangles together form a tessellating pattern.

Answers
  1 a Yes, interior angle is 60°, which divides exactly into 360°
    b Yes, interior angle is 90°, which divides exactly into 360°
    c No, interior angle is 108°, which does not divide exactly into 360°
    d Yes, interior angle is 120°, which divides exactly into 360°
    e No, interior angle is 135°, which does not divide exactly into 360°
  2 For example:

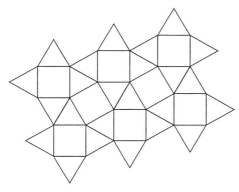

Framework objectives – Constructing right-angled triangles

Use straight edge and compasses to construct a triangle, given right angle, hypotenuse and side (RHS).

Use ICT to explore constructions of triangles and other 2-D shapes.

Oral and mental starter

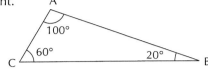

- On the board or OHP, sketch a scalene triangle as in the diagram on the right.
- Ask the class the following questions.
  - ○ Which is the largest angle? (Answer: 100°)
  - ○ Which is the smallest angle? (Answer: 20°)
  - ○ Which is the longest side? (Answer: BC)
  - ○ Which is the shortest side? (Answer: AC)
- Ask the class what they have noticed about their answers.
- If required, the students can write in their books: 'For any triangle, the largest angle is opposite the longest side, and the smallest angle is opposite the shortest side.'

Main lesson activity

- Remind the class about the three ways in which dimensions are given for constructing triangles, which they used in Year 7 and Year 8.

  - ○ Two sides and the included angle are given (SAS).

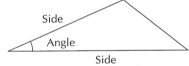

  - ○ Two angles and the included side are given (ASA).

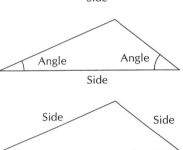

  - ○ Three sides are given (SSS).

- Tell the class that the lesson is about constructing right-angled triangles.
- Draw a right-angled triangle on the board or OHP, as on the right. Explain that the longest side of a right-angled triangle is called the **hypotenuse** and that it is always opposite the right angle.

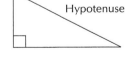

- Tell the class that they will be constructing triangles given a right angle, the hypotenuse and one of the other sides (RHS). For this, they will require a ruler and compasses.
- Draw a sketch of such a triangle on the board.
- Ask the students to draw the triangle in stages, as described below.
  - ○ Draw the line BC 4 cm long.
  - ○ Construct the perpendicular from B by first extending CB to a point D. Then with centre at B, draw arcs to intersect CD at X and Y. Setting your compasses to a larger radius, draw arcs with centres at X and Y to intersect at Z above B. Join BZ to make a right angle at B.
  - ○ Set your compasses to a radius of 5 cm and, with centre at C, draw an arc to intersect the perpendicular from B.
  - ○ The intersection of the arc and the perpendicular is A. Join AC to complete the triangle.

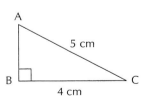

- **Note** The construction lines should be left on the diagram.

- **The class can now do Exercise 4E from Pupil Book 2.**

Exercise 4E Answers

2 **b** ≈ 9.5 m **c** ≈ 73° **3** **b** ≈ 31 km **c** ≈ 039°

Extension Answers

2 **c** Many different triangles can be constructed when only three angles are given
e Angle at B is required to construct the triangle

Plenary

- Ask the class in how many different ways the dimensions can be given for the construction of triangles, and to state them.
- Then ask them how these ways are expressed in the construction of right-angled triangles.

Key Words

- circumcentre
- circumcircle
- circumscribed
- hypotenuse

Homework

1 Construct each of the following right-angled triangles.

a

8 cm
5 cm

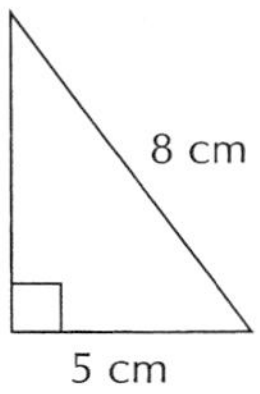

b

6.5 cm
6 cm

c

5.4 cm
7.2 cm

2 **a** Construct the right-angled triangle ABC.
b Measure the length of the line AB.
c Measure the size of angles A and C.

A
7 cm
B
C
4 cm

Answers
2 **b** AB ≈ 5.7 cm **c** ∠A ≈ 35°, ∠C ≈ 55°

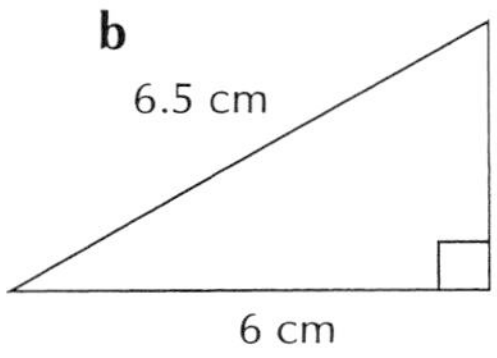

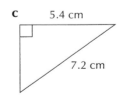

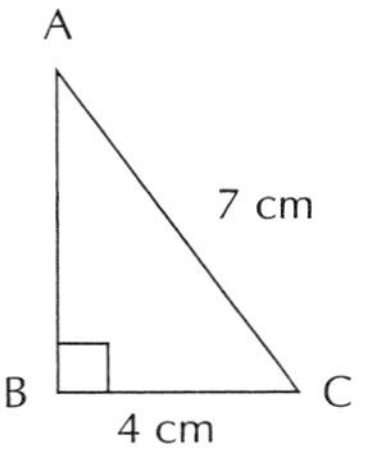

Framework objectives – Loci

Find the locus of a point that moves according to a simple rule, both by reasoning and by using ICT.

Oral and mental starter

- Tell the students to imagine a stick standing upright in the ground.
- Now tell them to imagine a fly moving around the stick, so that it is always exactly 5 cm from it.
- Ask the students to describe the shape which shows all the different positions where the fly could be. Allow the students to work in pairs or groups and give them about 5 minutes to discuss their answer. (Answer: surface of a cylinder with a hemisphere on top.)

Main lesson activity

- Tell the class that the lesson is about finding loci for more complicated situations than those they met in Year 8.
- Remind them that a locus is the movement of a point according to a given set of conditions or a rule.
- Go over the two important constructions of Example 4.6 in Pupil Book 2, which can now be stated to be loci.

- The locus of a point which is always equidistant from each of two fixed points A and B is the perpendicular bisector of the line joining the two points.

- The locus of a point which is equidistant from two fixed lines AB and BC, which meet at B, is the bisector of the angle ABC.

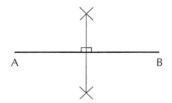

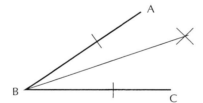

- Explain that a locus can sometimes be a region, as shown in the three examples below.
  - ○ A point which moves so that it is always 5 cm from a fixed point X has a locus which is a circle of radius 5 cm, with its centre at X.

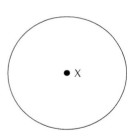

  - ○ The locus of a set of points which are 5 cm or less from a fixed point X is the region inside a circle of radius 5 cm, with its centre at X.

    Note that the region usually is shaded.

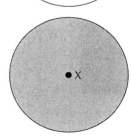

  - ○ The locus of a set of points that are less than 5 cm from a fixed point is the region inside a circle of radius 5 cm, with its centre at X.

    Note that the boundary usually is drawn as a dashed line to show that the points which are exactly 5 cm from X are not to be included.

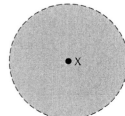

- **The class can now do Exercise 4F from Pupil Book 2.**

Exercise 4F Answers

3 a

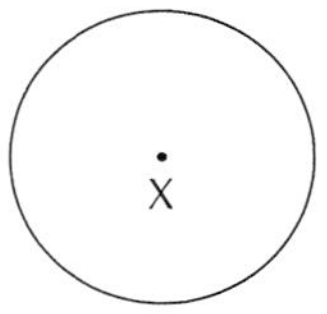
X

b

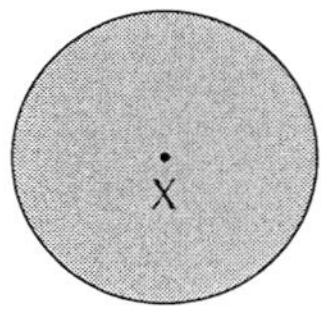
X

c

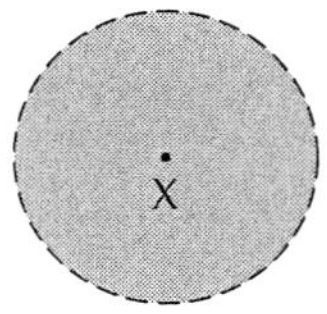
X

4

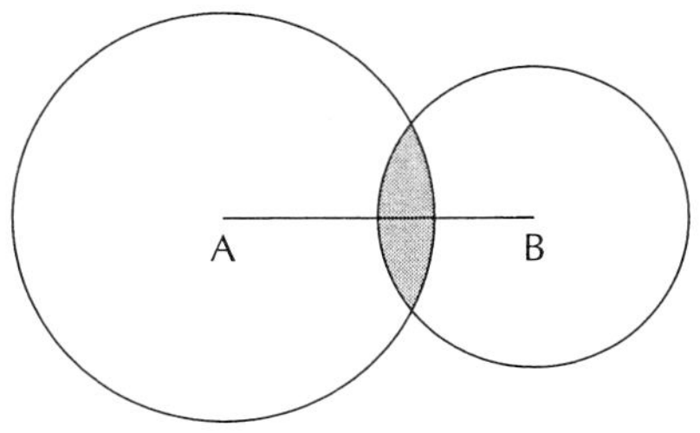
A
B

5

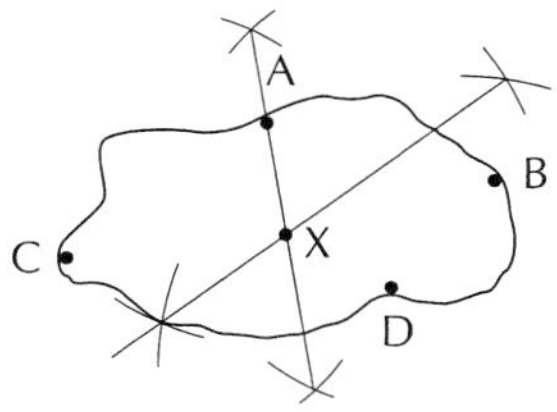
A
B
C
X
D

6

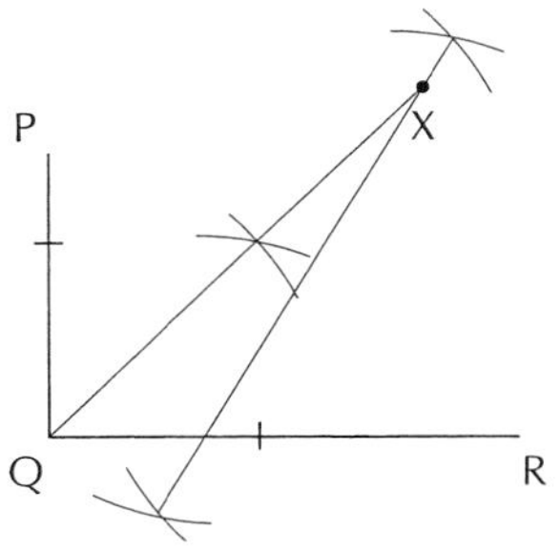
P
X
Q
R

7

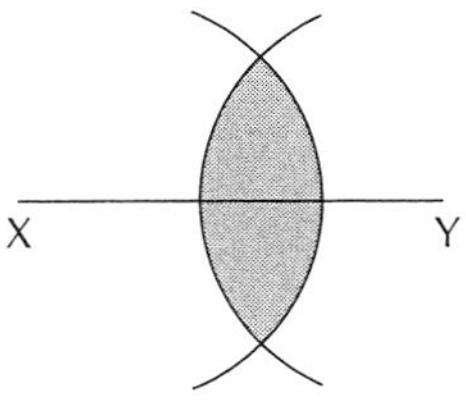
X
Y

8

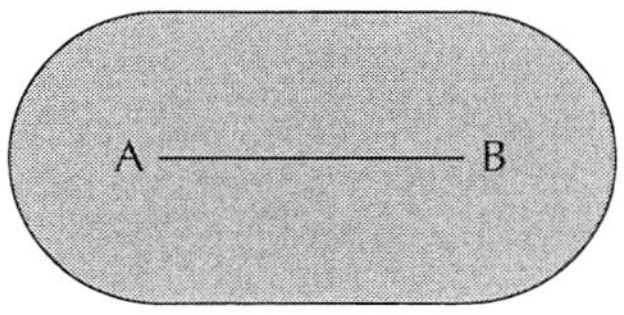
A
B

9

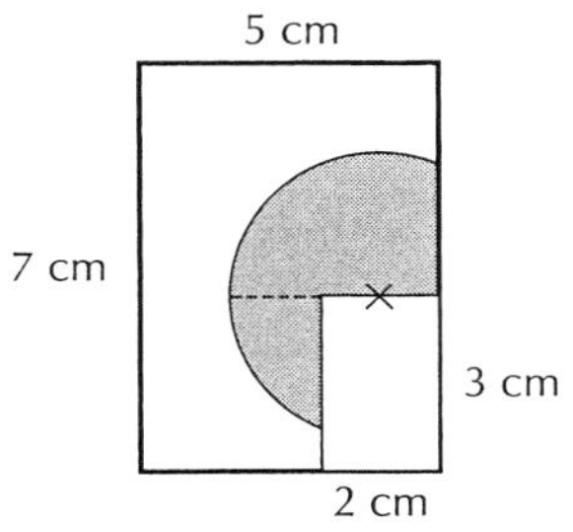
5 cm
7 cm
3 cm
2 cm

Extension Answers

1 Locus is a cycloid (see diagram)

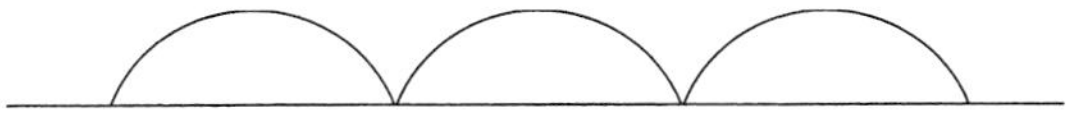

2 Locus is an arc of the circle whose radius is 3 m

Plenary

- Ask the class to give the definition of a locus.
- Then ask them to make up some examples of their own.

Key Words

- angle bisector
- perpendicular bisector
- equidistant
- locus
- loci
- region

Homework

1 Using a ruler and compasses, construct the locus which is equidistant from the points A and B.

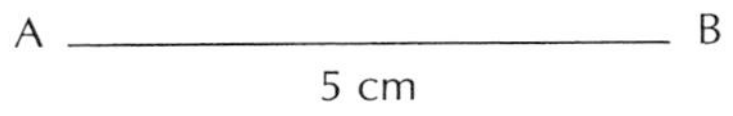
A
B
5 cm

2 Using a ruler and compasses, construct the locus which is equidistant from the perpendicular lines AB and BC.

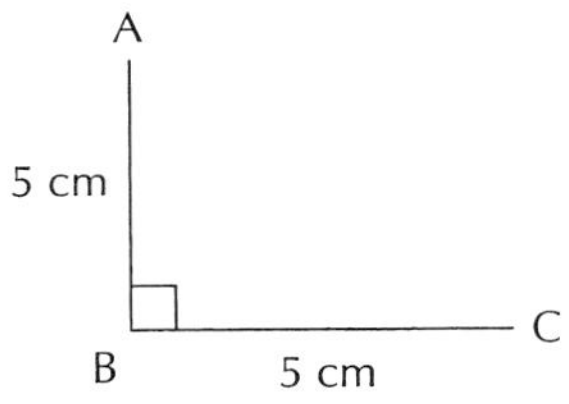
A
5 cm
B
5 cm
C

3 Draw a diagram to show the locus of a set of points which are 4 cm or less from a fixed point X.

4 Two alarm sensors, 6 m apart, are fitted to the side of a house, as shown below. The sensors can detect movement to a maximum distance of 5 m.

Draw a scale drawing to show the region that can be detected by both sensors. Use a scale of 1 cm to 1 m.

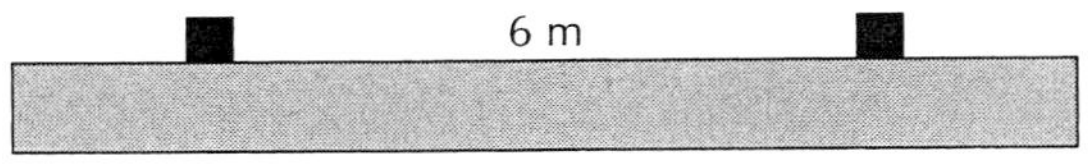
6 m

Answers

1 Perpendicular bisector of AB
2 Angle bisector of AB and BC
3 Shaded region inside the circle of radius 4 cm

4

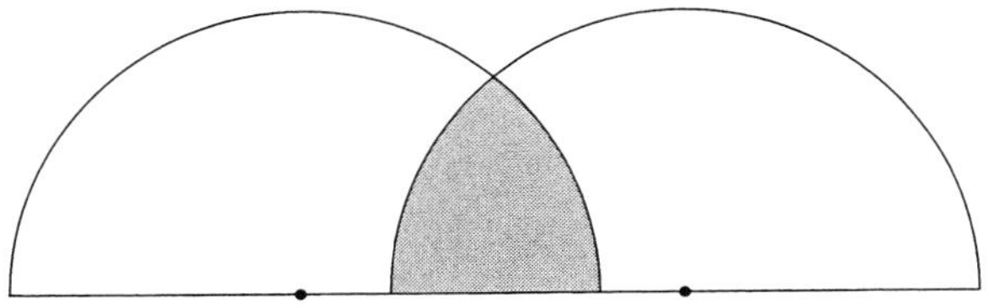

Oral and mental starter

- Tell the class that you are thinking of a 2-D shape. (Some examples are: a square, an isosceles triangle, a trapezium, a regular decagon, a circle.)
- Tell them that they can ask ten individual questions to guess exactly what the shape is and that you will answer only 'Yes' or 'No' to their questions.
- This activity can be repeated a number of times and made to suit the ability of the class.

Main lesson activity

- Emphasise that in geometry, as in all branches of mathematics, it is important that everyone involved in solving a problem agrees with all the facts which are used so that they all reach the same conclusions. Hence, the following terms, which are fundamental to all mathematical reasoning, should be explained to the class.
- **Convention** This is an agreed way of describing a mathematical situation. For example, it is a convention to label the end points of a line segment with capital letters. Any pair of different letters may be used.

A ——————— B

- **Definition** This is an exact description of something by its basic properties. For example, the definition of a square is a quadrilateral whose angles are all right angles and whose sides are equal in length.
  Sometimes, a definition is expressed as a symbol or a group of symbols, usually when it is too lengthy to write easily or conveniently.
- **Derived property** This is a property obtained from a definition. For example, a derived property from the definition of a square is its area, which is equal to the square of its side.
- **The class can now do Exercise 4G from Pupil Book 2.**

Exercise 4G Answers

1 a, c and d   2 a, b and c   3 b, c and e
4 For example:

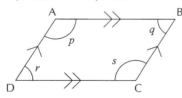

5 a Lines in the same plane which never meet and which are always the same distance apart
   b Closed 2-D shape whose sides are equal and whose interior angles are equal
   c Repeating pattern made on a plane surface from identical shapes which fit together exactly, leaving no gaps
   d Triangle whose sides are equal and whose interior angles are equal
   e 3-D shape whose faces are made from six plane squares with their sides all equal
6 For example: equal diagonals, diagonals perpendicular, opposite sides parallel, four lines of symmetry, rotational symmetry of order 4

Plenary

- Draw a rectangle on the board and write the word RECTANGLE below it.
- Ask the students to explain any conventions which are used to describe a rectangle.
- Then ask them to give the definition of a rectangle.
- Finally, ask for some derived properties of a rectangle.

Key Words

☐ **convention**
☐ **definition**
☐ **derived property**

Extension Answers

1 For example: copy one angle on tracing paper, which is then placed over the other angle
2 In the polygon on the right, the marked angles are its exterior angles. Face in the direction AB and turn through angle a to face in the direction BC. Turn through angle b to face in direction CD … and so on. Having turned through all the exterior angles, you will again be facing in the direction AB. That is, you have rotated through 360°. Hence, the sum of the exterior angles of any polygon is 360°

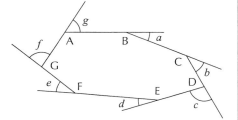

3 Draw a triangle, cut it out and then tear off two of the angles. Place these together to show that they make the exterior angle of the third angle
4 Make accurately ten regular hexagons of the same size. Show that they fit together to form a pattern with no gaps
5 Draw a rectangle and insert both diagonals and the bisectors of the sides. Then use a mirror to show that there are only two lines of symmetry – the bisectors of the sides

SATs Answers

2 **a** Sum of interior angles of a triangle = 180°, so 2 × 180° = 360°   **b** 540°   **c** 900°
3 **a** 50°   **b** ∠BED = 120°, ∠EBD = 30°, ∠BDE = 30°. As ∠EBD = ∠BDE, triangle BDE is isosceles

4

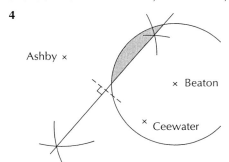

5

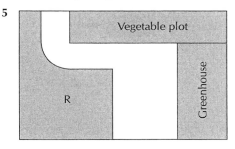

Homework

1 Which of the following statements are conventions?

  a Lower-case letters are used to define a line segment.

  b The horizontal axis on a coordinate grid is labelled x.

  c The symbol ∠ is used to denote an angle.

  d Coordinates are given in square brackets [ ].

2 Which of the following statements are definitions?

  a A complete turn is 360°.

  b A square has four sides.

  c A translation is a way of transforming a shape.

  d Congruent shapes are exactly the same shape and size.

3 Which of the following statements are derived properties?

  a A circle has a radius and a diameter.

  b In parallel lines intersected by a straight line, corresponding angles are equal.

  c The perpendicular height of a triangle is denoted by the letter h.

  d The diagonals of a rectangle are equal in length.

4 AB is parallel to CD and XY is a transversal.

  a Write down a convention for parallel lines.

  b Write down a definition for parallel lines.

  c Write down a derived property for parallel lines.

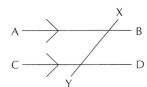

Answers
  1 **b** and **c**   2 **a** and **d**   3 **b** and **d**
  4 **a** Arrows are used to indicate parallel lines
    b Lines in the same plane which never meet and which are always the same distance apart
    c For example: alternate angles are equal, corresponding angles are equal, vertically opposite angles are equal

Handling Data 1

Framework objectives – Statistical investigations

Suggest a problem to explore using statistical methods, frame questions and raise conjectures.

Discuss how data relate to a problem. Identify possible sources, including primary and secondary data.

Design a survey or experiment to capture the necessary data from one or more sources. Determine the sample size and degree of accuracy needed. Design, trial and if necessary refine data collection sheets.

Oral and mental starter

- The students can work in small groups for this activity
- Write the following sources of information on a sheet: Questionnaire, Printed tables in books, Internet, Computer database and Observation sheet.
- Give the students cards, or a list, containing the following topics.

Primary Data	**Secondary Data**
Number of left-handed students in the class	Long jump performances in international athletes
TV viewing habits of students	Car engine sizes
Reaction times of students	Populations of various countries
Whether students are better at catching with their left or right hand	Football results in Europe
	Price of different makes of second-hand cars
The amounts of pocket money received by males and females in school	

- They should discuss each topic and decide how best to investigate each one, using the sources given above.

Main lesson activity

- Explain to the class that the aim of the lesson is to look at how to plan a statistical investigation.
- Point out that sometimes the most difficult part is to decide a topic to investigate. (Steps 1 and 2 in the table below.)
- Explain that to help them they will be given a planning sheet so that they may work systematically through their problem.
- Take an example of your choice or use the example given below.

Step	Example
1 Decide which general topic to study	The cost of housing in different parts of the UK
2 Specify in more detail	Comparing the costs in Wales and England
3 Consider questions which you could investigate	Is the average price higher in Wales? Is there a bigger difference in the prices in England than in Wales?
4 State your hypotheses (Your guesses at what could happen)	The price is higher in Wales There is more variation in price in England

5 Sources of information required	Internet. Estate agents. Building societies and banks mortgage reports. Government data: for example, Office for National Statistics http://www.statistics.gov.uk/
6 Relevant data	Average house prices in different counties of Wales and England
7 Possible problems	Counties of different sizes may affect the average unfairly, causing your data to be biased
8 Data collection	Make sure that your sample size is big enough to draw valid conclusions
9 Decide on level of accuracy required	If results are within, say, £1000 pounds of each other, you may decide that the results do not support the hypothesis that the prices are different
10 Determine sample size	Make sure that you collect enough data from both countries
11 Construct tables for large sets of raw data in order to make work manageable	
12 Decide which statistics are most suitable	If there are a few extreme values, you may choose to ignore the mean, as this will distort the results

- You could now show the students the three examples in Pupil Book 2.
- **The class can now do Exercise 5A from Pupil Book 2.**

Exercise 5A Answers

Answers will vary but should be similar in style to the examples.

Plenary

Key Words

- Use a group's planning sheet to discuss the points on it.
- Ask other groups to contribute points that can be added to the planning sheet.
- Explain that the homework is to produce an individual plan for a different topic. The students could use ideas already used by other groups.

- questionnaire
- printed table
- database
- survey
- statistic
- bias
- census

Homework

Take a different topic to those already studied and prepare a new planning sheet.

Answers
Answers will vary but should be similar in style to the examples.

LESSON 5.2

Framework objectives – Scatter graphs and correlation

Select, construct and modify, on paper and using ICT, suitable graphical representation to progress an enquiry, including scatter graphs to develop further understanding of correlation. Identify key features in the data.

Oral and mental starter

- Write a simple, open, multiplication table on the board or OHP, as shown.
- Prompt the students to tell you how to complete it.
- Now add on an extra column, with zero.
- Complete the extra column, with the students' help.
- Prompt them to extend the table into negative numbers.
- Use patterns (for example, subtracting 3s in the first row) to complete the columns.
- Now prompt the students to fully extend the table downwards, as shown.
- Show the class that, using patterns, they have just proved the rules for multiplying positive and negative numbers: for example, + × − = −.

×	+3	+2	+1
+3			
+2			
+1			

×	+3	+2	+1	0	−1	−2	−3
+3	9	6	3	0	−3	−6	−9
+2	6	4	2	0	−2	−4	−6
+1	3	2	1	0	−1	−2	−3
0	0	0	0	0	0	0	0
−1	−3	−2	−1	0	1	2	3
−2	−6	−4	−2	0	2	4	6
−3	−9	−6	−3	0	3	6	9

×	+	0	−
+	+	0	−
0	0	0	0
−	−	0	+

Main lesson activity

- Introduce the class to the table below, which gives the rules for combining two scatter graphs, which have a common axis, to obtain the resulting correlation.

	Positive correlation	No correlation	Negative correlation
Positive correlation	Positive	No correlation	Negative
No correlation	No correlation	*Cannot tell*	No correlation
Negative correlation	Negative	No correlation	Positive

As can be seen from the table, the resulting graph can have its axes in either order, as this does not affect the correlation.

An easy way to remember these rules is by comparing them with the rules for multiplying together positive and negative numbers, as shown below.

Multiply (×)	+	0	−
+	+	0	−
0	0	*The exception*	0
−	−	0	+

- Combining two graphs showing no correlation can be misleading, as the answer could be a graph with either positive, negative or no correlation. Hence you cannot tell just by using the rules.

Take, for example, the case of the fish caught off Rhyl.

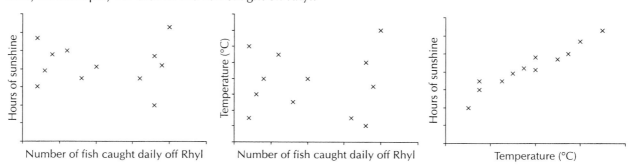

In this example, the two left-hand graphs show no correlation but combining hours of sunshine with temperature gives a positive correlation.

- Tell the class that *n* students' marks were collected from their tests in three different subjects, and two scatter graphs created. Then put these graphs on the board.
- Ask the class to tell you what the subject of each test could be.
- Then tell the class that they are actually Mathematics (Test A), Science (Test B) and Art (Test C).
- Invite them to discuss the correlation between the Mathematics and Science scores, and between the Mathematics and Art scores.
- Now prompt the class to tell you the correlation between the Science and the Art scores. In this case, there would be negative correlation.
- Now ask them to look at the rules for combining two correlation graphs in Pupil Book 2. They could copy into their books the table for correlations and the table for multiplying together positive and negative numbers.
- Point out how similar the rules are, but emphasise the exception to the rule, namely, two graphs, each showing no correlation, do not necessarily mean that the derived graph would have no correlation.

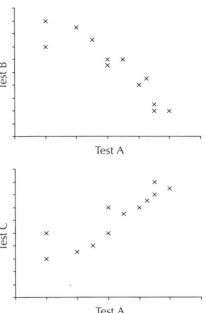

- **The class can now do Exercise 5B from Pupil Book 2.**

Exercise 5B Answers

1

Correlation between Q and R		
a Negative	**d** Cannot tell	**g** Negative
b No correlation	**e** Positive	**h** No correlation
c Positive	**f** No correlation	**i** No correlation

2 a Positive correlation **b** No correlation **c** No correlation
3 a Negative correlation **b** Negative correlation **c** Positive correlation

Plenary

- Finish the lesson with a short test of multiplications of positive and negative whole numbers, to reinforce the rules for combining two scatter graphs.

1 $+8 \times -3$	**2** -6×-5	**3** $+11 \times 0$	**4** -13×-13	**5** $+8 \times -6$
6 -9×-4	**7** $0 \times +14$	**8** $+15 \times -15$	**9** $+14 \times +14$	**10** -7×-10

Answers

1 -24	**2** 30	**3** 0	**4** 169	**5** -48
6 36	**7** 0	**8** -225	**9** 196	**10** 70

Homework

1 The test results of ten students are recorded for four different subjects. Here are the results.

Student	French	Spanish	English	Music
A	45	52	63	35
B	64	60	56	45
C	22	30	46	58
D	75	80	70	30
E	47	60	55	42
F	15	24	40	50
G	80	74	68	42
H	55	65	53	48
I	85	77	75	41
J	33	47	51	50

- **a** Plot the data for French and Spanish on a scatter graph.
- **b** Describe the relationship between French and Spanish.
- **c** Plot the data for English and Music on a scatter graph.
- **d** Describe the relationship between English and Music.
- **e** Plot the data for Spanish and English on a scatter graph.
- **f** Describe the relationship between Spanish and English.
- **g** Use your answers to parts **d** and **f** to state the correlation between Music and Spanish.

Answers
b Positive correlation **d** Negative correlation **f** Positive correlation **g** Negative correlation

LESSON 5.3

Framework objectives – Time series graphs

Select, construct and modify, on paper and using ICT, suitable graphical representation to progress an enquiry, including line graphs for time series.

Identify key features present in the data.

Oral and mental starter

- Ask individual students to give different units of time. You may need to give an example, such as months.
- Write any correct answers on the board or OHP.
- For each example, draw a horizontal scale and put a few labels on it, as shown on the right.
- Other examples which they may offer could include year, season, hour and days of the week.

Main lesson activity

- Tell the class that the aim is to look at different types of graph involving time.
- Explain that for all the types of graph which they are going to look at or produce, the time axis is *always* the horizontal axis.
- Invite the class to look at Graph 1 in Pupil Book 2 (Mean temperature difference from normal for the UK in 2002).
- Ask them to give some facts from the graph. For example, in 10 out of 12 months, the mean temperature was above normal; February and March showed the greatest differences. You could prompt them by asking what they can tell you about February and March.
- Then ask the students to look at the winter months and the summer months and compare the weather. They should observe that there are bigger temperature changes in the winter months.
- Now tell the class that you want them to look at the other graphs in Pupil Book 2. This activity could be done individually or in small groups. Suggest that they write down any key features of the graphs.
- **The class can now do Exercise 5C from Pupil Book 2.**

1 **a** Time becomes shorter **b** $\frac{3}{4}$ **c** After third bounce
   d In theory, the ball never comes to rest. In practice, it would eventually stop bouncing
2 **a** Mean temperature was exceeded on 10 months out of 12. Extreme changes in temperature were greater above normal (about 3.3 °C) than below normal (about −1.2 °C)
   b As data is for only one year, this could be exceptional. Data would need to be recorded over at least 10 years for valid conclusions to be drawn.
3 **a** June **b** September
   c Different pattern for average rainfall each month and different pattern for number of days of rain each month
   d Perth (approx values) 16 + 19 + 26 + 51 + 87 + 114 + 121 + 106 + 90 + 65 + 50 + 28 = 773. Brisbane (approx values) 86 + 95 + 94 + 73 + 70 + 50 + 49 + 43 + 44 + 66 + 67 + 75 = 812. So, Brisbane has 39 more days of rainfall.

Plenary

- Choose a graph and ask a group to list some key features.
- Ask the other students to add to it.
- Explain that when there are two similar graphs, such as two rainfall graphs, it is important to compare them, looking for both similarities and differences.

Key Words

- [ ] **time series**
- [ ] **graph**
- [ ] **raw data**
- [ ] **key feature**
- [ ] **line graph**

Homework

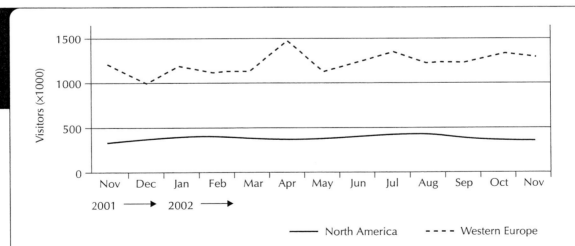

Write a brief report on the similarities and differences between the visits from the UK to North America and Western Europe. Make at least three statements. Try to give reasons for your answers.

Answers
More UK people visit Western Europe than North America (three to four times more), probably because Western Europe is nearer, so the costs are less. There is greater variation in the number of visitors for Western Europe from month to month (April being the most popular month). July and August are the most popular months to visit North America.

Framework objectives – Two-way tables

Design and use two-way tables.

Oral and mental starter

- Put the class into small groups of four or five students.
- Give the groups a mental test of ten questions. Appoint one person from each group as team captain to record a team's answer to each question.
- After the answers have been given, ask the team captains to record their answers in a two-way table on the board or OHT, using ticks for correct answers, as shown.

Group	Q1	Q2	Q3	Q4	Q5	Q6	Q7	Q8	Q9	Q10
1	✓		✓	✓		✓			✓	✓
2	✓	✓	✓		✓	✓			✓	
3		✓		✓			✓	✓	✓	

Test

1 £4.99 × 4
2 25% of 60
3 $\frac{1}{2}$ of a $\frac{1}{2}$
4 600 × 4000
5 72 ÷ 0.2
6 What is the HCF of 36 and 48?
7 Write down one answer to $x^2 + x = 0$
8 Increase £132 by 20%
9 What is the square root of 196?
10 Give both solutions to $(5 + x)^2 = 81$

Answers

1 £19.96
2 15
3 $\frac{1}{4}$
4 2 400 000
5 360
6 12
7 $x = 0$ or $x = -1$
8 £158.40
9 14 or –14
10 $x = 4$ and $x = -14$

Main lesson activity

- Keeping the students in their groups, explain that their task is to collect data from the whole class and record it.
- Use the data collection sheets as shown below, or the students can design their own.
- One student from each group is the 'collector', the rest of the group are the 'informers'. Each 'collector' goes from group to group collecting their data.

Favourite subject	Boys	Girls
English		
Science		
Art		
Maths		

Favourite colour	Boys	Girls
Blue		
Red		
Yellow		
Green		

Favourite TV programme	Boys	Girls
Soap		
Drama		
Cartoon		
News		
Other		

Favourite music	Boys	Girls
Rock		
Pop		
Dance		
R n B		

Favourite food	Boys	Girls
Chips		
Salad		
Pizza		
Burger		

Favourite hobby	Boys	Girls
Sport		
Computer		
Music		

- Now use other combinations to form different two-way tables. For example:

		Favourite colour			
		Blue	**Red**	**Yellow**	**Green**
Favourite hobby	Sport				
	Computer				
	Music				

- Having collected their data, the students can record it in their books. In each case, ask the students to pick out a key feature. A key feature could be that the data appears random (no relationship between the two variables).
- **The class can now do Exercise 5D from Pupil Book 2.**

1 a

Condition	Difference between boxed and not boxed
Excellent	100% – 60% = 40%
Very good	80% – 50% = 30%
Good	60% – 40% = 20%
Average	40% – 25% = 15%
Poor	20% – 10% = 10%

b Boxed toys are worth more than unboxed toys but the percentage difference in value reduces as the condition deteriorates.

2 a For the age range 10 to12, a larger percentage of boys have mobile phones. For the age range 13 to 15, a larger percentage of girls have them. **b** As the boys and girls get older, both percentages increase.

3 In June, July and August, 252 birthdays but in November, December and January, 228 birthdays. This would support the claim. Answers may vary depending on how the data is analysed but the conclusion should be the same.

4 160 cm and above: 20 boys but only 16 girls. This would support the claim. Answers may vary depending on how the data is analysed but the conclusion should be the same.

Extension Answers

a $\frac{9}{40}$ **b** $\frac{31}{80}$ **c** $\frac{1}{10}$ **d** $\frac{67}{80}$ **e** $\frac{11}{16}$

Key Words
- two-way table
- relationship
- data
- tally
- frequency

Plenary

- Ask the class to select a table where they saw a relationship.
- Look at, for example, boys' favourite colour and boys' favourite music. Are their responses different from girls?
- Write any relationships on the board. Ask the class what they could do to test whether the results were representative of the school.

Homework

1 Two fair spinners are spun and the scores are added together to get a total score. This is recorded in the two-way table, shown below.

	Second spinner			
	+	1	2	3
First spinner	1	2	3	
	2	3		
	3			
	4			

a Compete the table of total scores.
b List all the total scores which are prime numbers.
c State the most likely total scores.
d Write down the probability of getting a total score of 7. Give your answer as a fraction in its simplest form.
e Write down the probability of getting a total score of 5. Give your answer as a fraction in its simplest form.

2 A year group recorded the days of the week on which they were born. Here are the results.

Day	Boys	Girls
Monday	23	19
Tuesday	19	25
Wednesday	27	28
Thursday	31	26
Friday	35	41
Saturday	14	17
Sunday	12	11
Total	161	167

a Write a comment on the births of boys and girls.
b Write a comment about the number of births on different days of the week.

Answers
1 a

	Second spinner			
	+	1	2	3
First spinner	1	2	3	4
	2	3	4	5
	3	4	5	6
	4	5	6	7

b 2, 3, 5 and 7 **c** 4 and 5 **d** $\frac{1}{12}$ **e** $\frac{1}{4}$
2 a Each day, number of births of boys is close to that of girls
b Fewer births on Saturdays and Sundays

LESSON 5.5

Oral and mental starter

- Write £20 000 on the board. Explain to the class that you have seen an advert for a brand new car and £20 000 is the price.
- Now use Show me cards and ask the students to write on their cards what they think the value of the car will be in one year's time.
- Identify the smallest and biggest answers. Ask a student to tell you the range of these.
- Ask a student to explain why he/she gave, for example, £15 000.
- Now repeat, but this time they have to work in pairs and agree a value between them.
- Again look at the range of answers. Hopefully, it will be less than before.
- Ask a student to explain why the range is now less.
- This exercise can be repeated for different items: for example, a tin of beans costing 35p now.

Main lesson activity

- Tell the class that the objective of this lesson is to compare graphs or charts. They have to extract important information from them and comment on the differences between them.
- Ask the students to look at the two graphs about the values of cars given in Pupil Book 2, page 83.
- Ask questions, such as: 'Which car had a lower value after one year?', 'Which car was worth only £3000 after four years?', 'If you were buying car A or car B second-hand and you wanted the cheaper one, which would you buy?'
- Now ask the students to draw a graph of a car whose price starts at £20 000 and loses £4000 in value every year.
- Ask a student to explain why this is impossible. Prompt the response that after six years the car would have a negative value.
- Now draw a percentage bar chart.
- Ask how many of the students walk home after school.
- Mark off the approximate percentage on the bar. Shade it in.
- Now draw another percentage bar on the chart. Tell the class that another group which you teach gave a different result. Mark this result on the bar.
- Ask the class to compare the two bars.
- **The class can now do Exercise 5E from Pupil Book 2.**

  Note Lines of best fit are covered in Pupil Book 3 and Teacher Book 3 for Year 9. SATs Question 5 can be answered by students without knowing the concept, but some teachers may wish to instruct their students to omit this question.

Exercise 5E Answers

1 Greater proportion of children at rock concert
2 Science test was more difficult as only 10 students scored more than 40 marks
3 **a** More trains tend to be late 6 am – 10 am, 4 pm – 8 pm (rush hours)
  b All trains on time

Plenary

Key Words
- **comparison**
- **percentage bar chart**
- **distribution**

- Describe two villages to the class, for each of which they have to sketch a pie chart.
  Village 1: half of the population is aged over 60 years, and one-third of the population is aged under 18 years.
  Village 2: there is a smaller proportion of over 60s than in village 1, but a larger proportion of under 18s.
- Ask the students to compare their pie charts with each other to see whether they have interpreted the data correctly. There will be slight differences between their answers.

Homework

1 Here are two sets of test results for 60 students.

Percentage mark	Number of students	
	French	Art
0–20	5	12
21–40	8	11
41–60	21	14
61–80	16	12
81–100	10	11

a Draw a pie chart for each subject.

b Compare the results for French and art.

2 A survey was carried out about the favourite cheese of men and women. Here are the results.

	Red	White
Men	65%	35%
Women	30%	70%

a Draw a percentage bar chart to represent these data.

b Compare the results for men and women.

Answers

1 **a**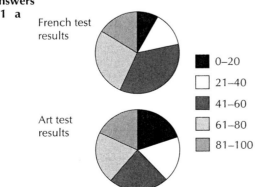

French test results
Art test results

0–20
21–40
41–60
61–80
81–100

b Art results are more evenly spread than French results.

2 **a**

Cheese preference

White
Red

Men   Women

b Men prefer red and women prefer white.

CHAPTER 6

Shape, Space and Measures 2

LESSON 6.1

Framework objectives – Circumference of a circle
Use units of measurement to calculate, estimate, measure and solve problems in a variety of contexts.

Oral and mental starter

- Revise the names and spelling of the various parts of a circle.
- First, ask the students to sketch a circle on their whiteboards or in their books. Then ask them to draw and label all the different parts of a circle which they can remember.
- Ask individual students to show the answers on their whiteboards, or to write separate answers on the board. Check their spelling.
- The following terms should be covered: centre, radius, diameter, arc, circumference, chord, sector, segment, and tangent.

Main lesson activity

- Explain to the class that they are going to undertake a practical activity to see whether there is a relationship between the length of the diameter and the circumference of a circle.
- It is suggested that the class should work in pairs. Each pair will require compasses, a 30 cm ruler and a piece of fine, high-quality string at least 40 cm in length.
- **The class can now do Exercise 6A from Pupil Book 2.**

Exercise 6A Answers

Circumference divided by diameter is slightly larger than 3. A simple relation is $C = 3d$

Extension Answers

Cone becomes taller.

Plenary

- Summarise what the class have discovered during the lesson.
- Explain that a simple relation between the circumference, C, of a circle and its diameter, d, is $C = 3d$.
- Tell the class that in the next lesson a more accurate formula for calculating a circumference will be given.

Key Words

- centre
- circumference
- radius
- diameter

Homework

1 Draw a circle of radius 5 cm. Cut it out and fold it in half.

a What do you notice about the fold line?

b How can you use this to find the centre of the circle?

2 a How many lines of symmetry does a circle have?

b What is the order of rotational symmetry for a circle?

Answers

1 a Forms a diameter

b Fold in half again to form a different diameter. Intersection of the diameters is the centre

2 a Infinite number **b** Infinity (∞)

LESSON 6.2

Oral and mental starter

- Invite the class to imagine two 10p coins, one of which is held still while the other coin is rolled around it so that the coins are always in contact.
- Now ask the class how many revolutions the moving coin will make before it returns to its starting position. (Answer: Two)

Main lesson activity

- Remind the class that in the last lesson they found that the **circumference**, C, of a circle with **diameter** d is given approximately by the formula $C = 3d$.
- Tell them that this lesson is about calculating a more accurate value for the circumference.
- Explain that the number by which the diameter has to be multiplied is slightly larger than 3. This special number is represented by the Greek letter π (pronounced *pi*). The value of π cannot be written down exactly as a fraction or a terminating decimal, so approximate values are used. The most common of these are:

  $\pi = \dfrac{22}{7}$ (as a fraction)

  $\pi = 3.14$ (as a decimal rounded to two decimal places)

  $\pi = 3.1416$ (as a decimal rounded to four decimal places)

  $\pi = 3.141\,592\,654$ (on a scientific calculator)
- Students who have scientific calculators should find the $\boxed{\pi}$ key.
- π has been calculated to millions of decimal places, using computers. So far, no repeating pattern has ever been found.
- The formula for calculating the circumference, C, of a circle with diameter d is written as:

  $C = \pi d$
- As the diameter is twice the **radius**, r, the circumference is also given by:

  $C = \pi d = \pi \times 2r = 2\pi r$
- When calculating the circumference, students should take π to be 3.14, or they should use the $\boxed{\pi}$ key on their calculators. Answers are usually given to one decimal place.
- Do some examples of calculating the circumference given the diameter or the radius.

- **The class can now do Exercise 6B from Pupil Book 2.**

Plenary

- Draw a circle on the board or on an OHT.
- Ask the class how they would find its area.
- They will probably say that you can estimate its area by counting the number of centimetre squares inside the circle.
- Explain that the area of a circle can be calculated using a formula that they will meet in the next lesson.

Key Words

- ☐ circumference
- ☐ diameter
- ☐ pi
- ☐ radius

Homework

Take $\pi = 3.14$ or use the π key on your calculator.

1 Calculate the circumference of each of the following circles. Give your answers to one decimal place.

a

5 cm

b

36 mm

c

1.9 m

2 The Earth has a radius of 6400 km. Calculate the distance round the equator, giving your answer to the nearest 100 kilometres.

3 A cylindrical can has a diameter of 12 cm.

What is the length of a label going round the can, if its ends overlap by 1 cm? Give your answer to one decimal place.

4 The diameter of each wheel on Sam's bike is 75 cm.

a Calculate the circumference of each wheel, giving your answer to the nearest centimetre.

b How many times does each wheel turn when Sam rides his bike for a distance of 2 km? Give your answer to the nearest 10 turns.

Answers
1 **a** 15.7 cm **b** 113.1 mm **c** 11.9 m
2 40 200 km
3 38.7 cm
4 **a** 236 cm **b** 850

LESSON 6.3

Framework objectives – Formula for the area of a circle

Know and use the formula for the area of a circle.

Oral and mental starter

- Invite the class to imagine a circle with radius of 5 cm which just fits inside a square.
- Now ask them to write down on their white boards the length of each side of the square. (Answer: 10 cm)
- Next, ask the class to write down the area of the square. (Answer: 100 cm²)
- Finally, ask them what this shows about the area of the circle. (Answer: Area of the circle must be less than 100 cm²)

Main lesson activity

- Tell the class that they are going to find the formula for the **area** of a circle.
- The method to be explained is best prepared on an OHT or already cut out from card.
- Show the class how a circle can be split into 16 equal sectors. When these are placed together, the resulting shape is roughly rectangular.

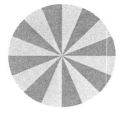 

- Explain that as the number of sectors is increased, the shape will eventually become a rectangle. The area of this rectangle will be the same as the area of the circle.
- Show that the length of this rectangle is half the circumference, C, of the circle, and its width is the **radius**, r, of the circle. Draw the diagram shown on the right.
- The area of the rectangle is given by:
$$A = \tfrac{1}{2}C \times r = \tfrac{1}{2} \times 2 \times \pi \times r \times r$$
$$= \pi \times r \times r = \pi r^2$$
- So, the formula for the area A of a circle of radius r is:
$$A = \pi r^2$$
- Do some examples of calculating the areas of circles given the radius or the diameter. Explain that the answers may sometimes need to be left in terms of π.
- Demonstrate the calculator operations for these examples. Point out that different calculators may require different keying.

- **The class can now do Exercise 6C from Pupil Book 2.**

Plenary

- Draw a circle on the board. Highlight the circumference and area, and ask the students to write down the formulae used to calculate them.
- Emphasise the need to learn these formulae, as they are not given in examinations.

Key Words

- ☐ **area**
- ☐ **diameter**
- ☐ **pi**
- ☐ **radius**

Homework

Take π = 3.14 or use the 🔲 π key on your calculator.

1 Calculate the area of each of the following circles. Give your answers to one decimal place.

a   2.4 cm

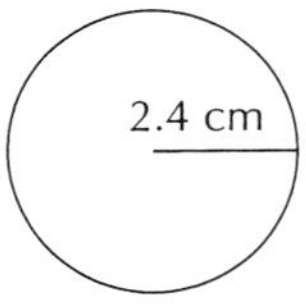

b   2.8 cm

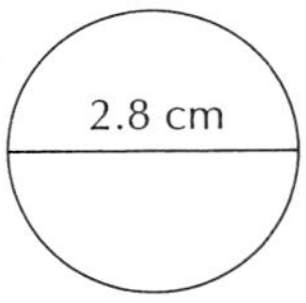

c   7.2 m

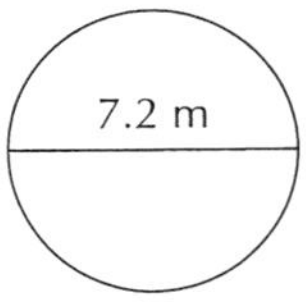

2 Find the area of a circle with a radius of 30 m. Give your answer in terms of π.

3 Calculate the area of a circular table with a diameter of 2.1 m. Give your answer to two decimal places.

4 Calculate the approximate area of Kate's semicircular brooch shown on the right.

Give your answer to one decimal place.

    3.2 cm

Answers
  1 **a** 18.1 cm²   **b** 6.2 cm²   **c** 40.7 m²
  2 900π m²
  3 3.46 m²
  4 4.0 cm²

LESSON 6.4

Framework objectives – Metric units for area and volume

Use units of measurement to calculate, estimate, measure and solve problems in a variety of contexts. Convert between area measures (mm² to cm², cm² to m², and vice versa) and between volume measures (mm³ to cm³, cm³ to m³, and vice versa).

Oral and mental starter

- Multiplying and dividing by 10, 100, 1000 and 10 000 will be revised.
- On the board, draw the grid on the right, or use a prepared OHT.
- Tell the class that the starting number is 3.5.
- Ask individual students to point to the number that is:
  3.5×10 3.5×100 3.5×1000 $3.5 \times 10\,000$
- Then ask the class to explain the rules for multiplying by powers of 10.
- Next, ask individual students to point to the number that is:
  $3.5 \div 10$ $3.5 \div 100$ $3.5 \div 1000$ $3.5 \div 10\,000$
- Finally, ask the class to explain the rules for dividing by powers of 10.

35	0.0035	3500
0.000 35	**3.5**	0.35
350	0.035	35 000

Main lesson activity

- Tell the class that the lesson is about converting the metric units of area, volume and capacity.
- Remind them that the metric units for area are: the square millimetre (mm²), the square centimetre (cm²) and the square metre (m²).
- Draw two squares on the board and explain why $1 \text{ cm}^2 = 100 \text{ mm}^2$.
- Draw another two squares on the board and explain to the class why $1 \text{ m}^2 = 10\,000 \text{ cm}^2$.
- The students can now copy the following into their books:

  Metric units of area
100 mm²	= 1 cm²
10 000 cm²	= 1 m²
10 000 m²	= 1 hectare (ha)
1 hectare	= 100 ares

  Note that, for measuring the area of fields, the m² is too small, while the km² is too large. Hence, a more conveniently sized unit is used – the **are**, which is 100 m². Land area is usually given in units of 100 ares, where 100 ares = 1 hectare.
- Remind the class that the metric units for volume are: the cubic millimetre (mm³), the cubic centimetre (cm³) and the cubic metre (m³).
- Draw two cubes on the board and explain why $1 \text{ cm}^3 = 1000 \text{ mm}^3$.
- Draw another two cubes on the board and explain why $1 \text{ m}^3 = 1\,000\,000 \text{ cm}^3$.
- The students can now copy the following into their books:

  Metric units of volume
1000 mm³	= 1 cm³
1 000 000 cm³	= 1 m³

- Remind the class that the metric units for capacity are: the litre (l), the centilitre (cl) and the millilitre (ml). They can now copy the following into their books:

  Metric units of capacity
1 m³	= 1000 litres
1000 cm³	= 1 litre
1 cm³	= 1 millilitre

- Stress the following:
  ○ To convert from a large unit to a smaller unit, **always multiply** by the conversion factor.
  ○ To convert from a small unit to a larger unit, **always divide** by the conversion factor.

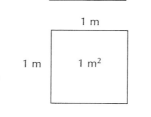
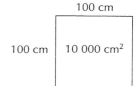
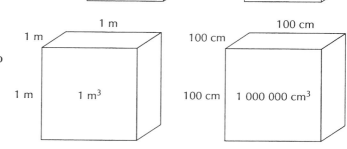
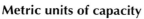

70

- Show the class the following examples of conversion.

    35 000 cm² to m²   0.35 cm³ to mm³   3500 cm³ to litres

  ○ 35 000 cm² = 35 000 ÷ 10 000 = 3.5 m²
  ○ 0.35 cm³ = 0.35 × 1000 = 350 mm³
  ○ 3500 cm³ = 3500 ÷ 1000 = 3.5 litres

- **The class can now do Exercise 6D from Pupil Book 2.**

Exercise 6D Answers

1 **a** 40 000 cm² **b** 70 000 cm² **c** 200 000 cm² **d** 35 000 cm² **e** 8000 cm²
2 **a** 200 mm² **b** 500 mm² **c** 850 mm² **d** 3600 mm² **e** 40 mm²
3 **a** 8 cm² **b** 25 cm² **c** 78.3 cm² **d** 5.4 cm² **e** 0.6 cm²
4 **a** 2 m² **b** 8.5 m² **c** 27 m² **d** 18.6 m² **e** 0.348 m²
5 **a** 3000 mm³ **b** 10 000 mm³ **c** 6800 mm³ **d** 300 mm³ **e** 480 mm³
6 **a** 5 m³ **b** 7.5 m³ **c** 12 m³ **d** 0.65 m³ **e** 0.002 m³
7 **a** 8 litres **b** 17 litres **c** 0.5 litre **d** 3000 litres **e** 7200 litres
8 **a** 8.5 cl **b** 120 cl **c** 84 ml **d** 4.5 litres **e** 2400 ml
9 160 **10 a** 10 800 m² **b** 1.08 hectares **11** 150 litres **12** 6 litres **13** 500

Extension Answers

1 250 **2 a** 1296 square inches **b** 46 656 cubic inches
3 4840 square yards ≈ 0.405 hectares

Plenary

- Write the following on the board and ask the students to fill in the blanks.

  1 _____ mm² = 1 cm²   4 _____ mm³ = 1 cm³   6 _____ litres = 1 m³
  2 _____ cm² = 1 m²   5 _____ cm³ = 1 m³   7 _____ cm³ = 1 litre
  3 _____ m² = 1 hectare (ha)

  Answers **1** 100 **2** 10 000 **3** 10 000 **4** 1000 **5** 1 000 000 **6** 1000
                7 1000

Key Words

- ☐ **square millimetre**
- ☐ **square centimetre**
- ☐ **square metre**
- ☐ **hectare**
- ☐ **cubic millimetre**
- ☐ **cubic centimetre**
- ☐ **cubic metre**
- ☐ **litre**

Homework

1 Express each of the following in mm².

   a 3 cm²   **b** 8 cm²   **c** 4.5 cm²   **d** 0.8 cm²

2 Express each of the following in m².

   a 40 000 cm²   **b** 70 000 cm²   **c** 32 000 cm²   **d** 5000 cm²

3 Express each of the following in cm³.

   a 2 m³   **b** 9 m³   **c** 3.7 m³   **d** 0.3 m³

4 Express each of the following in litres.

   a 8000 cm³   **b** 12 000 cm³   **c** 23 500 cm³   **d** 250 cm³

5 A rectangular park is 620 m long and 340 m wide. Find the area of the park in hectares.

6 Calculate the volume of the box on the right. Give your answer in litres.

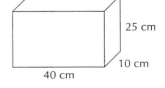

25 cm
10 cm
40 cm

Homework Answers
  1 **a** 300 mm² **b** 800 mm² **c** 450 mm² **d** 80 mm² **2 a** 4 m² **b** 7 m² **c** 3.2 m² **d** 0.5 m²
  3 **a** 2 000 000 cm³ **b** 9 000 000 cm³ **c** 3 700 000 cm³ **d** 300 000 cm³
  4 **a** 8 litres **b** 12 litres **c** 23.5 litres **d** 0.25 litre **5** 21.08 hectares **6** 10 litres

Framework objectives – Volume and surface area of prisms
Calculate the surface area and volume of right prisms.

Oral and mental starter

- Show the class various 3-D shapes such as: cube, cuboid, square-based pyramid, tetrahedron, triangular prism, cylinder, sphere.
- Ask them to identify each shape and the spelling of each name. Write all the names on the board.

Main lesson activity

- Tell the class that the lesson will show them how to find the volume and the surface area of prisms.
- Show them various prisms and ask them to explain what is similar about the shapes.
- Ask the class to write the definition of a prism into their books.
    A prism is a 3-D shape which has exactly the same 2-D shape running all the way through it.
- Explain that if a prism is cut through anywhere at right angles to its length, this 2-D shape will be seen. It is known as the **cross-section** of the prism.
- Ask the class to give some examples of prisms. (Packets, Toblerone chocolate box, stick of rock, door wedge.)
- Remind the class that a cuboid is an example of a prism. If available, show the class models of different prisms.
- Explain that the **volume**, V, of a prism is found by multiplying the area, A, of its cross-section by its length, l (or its height if the prism stands on one end).
- Next, explain how to calculate the total **surface area** of a prism by finding the sum of the areas of its faces. For example, in the first prism shown on the right, the total surface area is composed of the two end pentagons plus five rectangles.
- Use as an example, to calculate its total surface area and volume, the cuboidal prism shown on the right.
  (Answers: Surface area = 262 cm²; volume = 280 cm³)
- **The class can now do Exercise 6E from Pupil Book 2.**

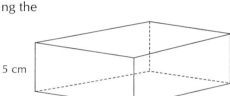

5 cm

7 cm   8 cm

Exercise 6E Answers

1 a i 68 cm^2 ii 24 cm^3 b i 684 cm^2 ii 864 cm^3 c i 146 m^2 ii 72 m^3
2 a 8000 mm^3 b 8 cm^3
3 a 3150 cm^3
4 a 61.5 m^2 b 922.5 m^3 c 922 500 litres
5 a 262 500 cm^3 b 0.26 m^3

Extension Answers

1 a 56.5 cm^3 b 106 m^3

SATs Answers

1 a A, C, D b 40 cm
2 a 50π cm or 157 cm b 137 m
3 a 225π cm^2 or 706.5 cm^2 b 19.1 cm (1 dp)
4 a 10.625 cm^2 b 37.1875 cm^3
5 a 168 cm^3 b 120 cm^3

Plenary

- Ask the students to give the definition of a prism.
- Then invite them to give some everyday examples of where they might see prisms.
- Ask individual students to explain how to find the surface area and the volume of a prism.

Key Words

- cross-section
- prism
- surface area
- volume

Homework

1 Calculate **i** the total surface area and **ii** the volume of each of the following prisms.

a

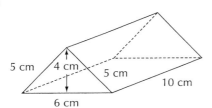

b

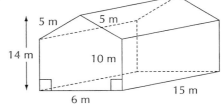

2 A child's toy brick has a cross-section of area 850 mm^2 and is 8 mm high.

a Calculate the volume of the brick, giving your answer in cubic millimetres.

b Write down the volume of the brick in cubic centimetres.

3 The diagram shows the measurements of the cross-section of a water trough. The length of the trough is 3 m.

a Calculate the volume of the trough.

b How many litres of water can the trough hold when it is full?

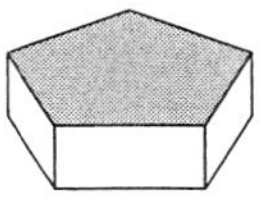

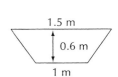

Answers
1 a i 184 cm^2 ii 120 cm^3 b i 684 m^2 ii 1080 m^3
2 a 6800 mm^3 b 6.8 cm^3
3 a 2.25 m^3 b 2250 litres

Number 2

CHAPTER 7

Framework objectives – Powers of 10

Extend knowledge of integer powers of 10.

Multiply and divide by any integer power of 10.

Oral and mental starter

- Have available prepared cards or write on the board.
- Show a calculator display. Ask the students to write the number out in full. (White boards are useful for this, or students can write in their exercise books.) Take, for example:

$$3.8^{-03}$$

- Some students may need to have this explained. Namely, the power gives the number of places to move the digits. Negative powers mean move to the right, positive powers mean move to the left. Students may prefer to 'see' the decimal point shifting, in which case a negative power moves the point to the left and a positive power moves the point to the right.
- Check their answers and then give (or display) the answer.
- If the students are writing in their exercise books, ten or more examples can be given before checking their answers.

Main lesson activity

- This lesson recalls working with powers of 10 and follows on from the Oral and mental starter.
- Write up a problem, such as 6.3×100. Ask the students for the answer (630), and to explain how they got it. They are likely to talk about moving the decimal point. In the context of this lesson, this may be the best way to see what is happening but the students should be reminded that it is the digits which move.
- Now write up another problem, such as 7.8×10^2. Ask the students for the answer (780) and also what connection there is with the previous example. (The power and the number of zeros give the number of places which the digits move.)
- Do the same with $0.32 \div 1000$ and $0.32 \div 10^3$. (Answer: 0.000 32)
- Next, write up a third problem, such as 67.2×0.01. Ask the students for the answer (0.672), and to explain how they got it.
- Discuss any similarities with previous examples. They may realise that multiplying by 0.01 is the same as dividing by 100 or 10^2.
- Now write up a problem such as $54.3 \div 0.1$. Ask the students for the answer (543), and to explain how they got it.
- Discuss any similarities with previous examples. They may realise that dividing by 0.1 is the same as multiplying by 10.
- Do more examples if necessary and/or get the students to copy the following table.

Multiplying/dividing by	Is the same as dividing/multiplying by
1000 or 10^3	0.001 or 10^{-3}
100 or 10^2	0.01 or 10^{-2}
10	0.1
0.1 or 10^{-1}	10

- **The class can now do Exercise 7A from Pupil Book 2.**

1 a i 8700 **ii** 87 000 **b i** 320 **ii** 3200 **c i** 103 500 **ii** 1 035 000
d i 90 **ii** 900 **e i** 23 060 **ii** 230 600
2 a i 0.0087 **ii** 0.000 87 **b i** 0.000 32 **ii** 0.000 032 **c i** 0.1035 **ii** 0.010 35
d i 0.000 09 **ii** 0.000 009 **e i** 0.023 06 **ii** 0.002 306
3 a i 270 **ii** 2700 **b i** 45 **ii** 450 **c i** 20 700 **ii** 207 000 **d i** 8 **ii** 80
e i 4170 **ii** 41 700
4 a i 0.027 **ii** 0.0027 **b i** 0.0045 **ii** 0.000 45 **c i** 2.07 **ii** 0.207
d i 0.0008 **ii** 0.000 08 **c i** 0.417 **ii** 0.0417
5 a 634 **b** 0.473 **c** 66 000 **d** 0.0027 **e** 30 760 000 **f** 0.7193 **g** 0.92
h 6.4 **i** 0.0084 **j** 871 **k** 376 **l** 0.0023 **m** 9000 **n** 0.003 09 **o** 235
p 0.000 001
6 a i 0.1 **ii** 0.01 **iii** 0.001 **iv** 0.0001 **b i** 0.92 **ii** 0.000 71 **iii** 0.456
iv 42 **v** 98 **vi** 2140
7 a 0.088 **b** 53 200 **c** 0.003 14 **d** 0.903

Extension Answers

a i 4 milligrams **ii** 8 megawatts **iii** 75 centilitres
c 29.8 cm

Plenary

- Reverse the Oral and mental starter.
- Put a number on the board such as 640. Ask the students to write it as a
  calculator display: 6.4×10^2
- Repeat with other numbers such as 0.0067, 8900, 0.53, 510 000.

Key Words

- ☐ **power of ten**
- ☐ **place value**
- ☐ **equivalent operation**
- ☐ **inverse operation**

Homework

1 Multiply each of the following numbers by **i** 10^2 and **ii** 10^4.

    a 5.8   **b** 0.95   **c** 86.2

2 Divide each of the following numbers by **i** 0.1 and **ii** 0.001.

    a 3.1   **b** 0.68   **c** 302

3 Calculate:

    a 5.87×100 **b** $52.9 \div 10$ **c** 98×100 **d** $23.7 \div 1000$

Answers
  1 a i 580 **ii** 58 000 **b i** 95 **ii** 9500 **c i** 8620 **ii** 862 000
  2 a i 31 **ii** 3100 **b i** 6.8 **ii** 680 **c i** 3020 **ii** 302 000
  3 a 587 **b** 5.29 **c** 9800 **d** 0.0237

LESSON

7.2

Framework objectives – Rounding

Use rounding to make estimates.

Round numbers to the nearest whole number or to one or two decimal places.

Oral and mental starter

- Using a target board such as the one shown, ask the students to round the numbers so that only one non-zero digit, plus some zeros, if necessary, remain.
- The students may need to be shown with a few examples. For example, for the top row the answers are 5, 0.08, 1, 3, 0.6.
- Now ask them, either as a group or individually, to round the rest to **one significant figure**. This terminology may be used if appropriate for the group.
- Next, repeat with rounding so that two non-zero digits (and zeros) remain. Once again, this may need some examples. For the top row the answers are 4.7, 0.075, 1.1, 3.2, 0.58.
- Finally, ask the students, either as a group or individually, to round the rest to **two significant figures**.

4.652	0.0752	1.071	3.222	0.578
0.0825	1.629	11.635	3.999	4.814
3.421	8.525	3.688	9.002	1.035
6.455	1.459	1.291	5.927	2.716

Main lesson activity

- This is a review lesson on rounding and estimation.
- Start with rounding some numbers to one and two decimal places. For example:
  2.367 = 2.4 (1 dp) = 2.37 (2 dp)   0.825 = 0.8 (1 dp) = 0.83 (2 dp)
- The students should be familiar with this but do more examples if necessary.
- Now ask them to round 56 to the nearest number with just one non-zero digit and one or more zeros. (Refer to Oral and mental starter.) (Answer: 60)
- Repeat with 489 (500), 0.31 (0.3), 0.0065 (0.007), 0.99 (1).
- Introduce, if not already mentioned in the Oral and mental starter, the terminology **one significant figure**.
- Now ask the students to round 563 to a number with two non-zero digits and one or more zeros. (Answer: 560)
- Introduce, if not already mentioned in the Oral and mental starter, the terminology **two significant figures**.
- Now round the following numbers to two significant figures: 489 (490), 0.0356 (0.036), 0.99 (1.0).
- Ask for an estimate of 32% of £529. The answers may well be guessed but ask for a method. For example, round to one significant figure to give:
  $$32\% \text{ of } £529 \approx 30\% \text{ of } £500$$
  $$= 3 \times 10\% \text{ of } £500$$
  $$= 3 \times £50 = £150$$
- Repeat with $2.3^2 \div 0.398$
  $$\approx 2^2 \div 0.4$$
  $$= 4 \div 0.4$$
  $$= 40 \div 4 = 10$$
- Do more examples if necessary.
- **The class can now do Exercise 7B from Pupil Book 2.**

Plenary

● Ask the students if they know the term 'ball-park figure'.
● Obtain from them (or tell them) that it means an approximate value. The term comes from the USA, where the attendance at a baseball game was given approximately before accurate counting became possible.
● Ask the students 'if the attendance at a football match were given as 42 000 to the nearest 1000, what could the limits of the crowd be?' 41 500 and 42 499 (accept 42 500).
● Repeat with the limits of 500 kg to the nearest 100 kg (450–550), 16 cm to the nearest cm (15.5–16.5), 1.7 to one decimal place (1.65–1.75).

Key Words

☐ rounding
☐ approximation
☐ decimal place
☐ significant figure

Homework

1 Round each of the following numbers to **i** one decimal place and **ii** two decimal places.

  a 4.678   **b** 19.198   **c** 9.054   **d** 32.891

2 Round the numbers in Question **1** to one significant figure.

3 Estimate the answer to each of the following.

  a 29% of £419   **b** 12.2 ÷ 0.048   **c** $\dfrac{58.9 \times 33.2}{46.7 - 15.8}$

Answers
  1 a i 4.7 **ii** 4.68 **b i** 19.2 **ii** 19.20 **c i** 9.1 **ii** 9.05 **d i** 32.9 **ii** 32.89
  2 a 5 **b** 20 **c** 9 **d** 30
  3 a £120 **b** 200–250 **c** 60

Framework objectives – Recurring decimals
Know that a recurring decimal is an exact fraction.

$\frac{1}{2}$	$\frac{3}{7}$	$\frac{7}{20}$	$\frac{2}{3}$	$\frac{13}{18}$
$\frac{11}{30}$	$\frac{7}{12}$	$\frac{43}{50}$	$\frac{3}{8}$	$\frac{7}{9}$
$\frac{3}{11}$	$\frac{3}{4}$	$\frac{1}{28}$	$\frac{12}{25}$	$\frac{5}{6}$
$\frac{9}{25}$	$\frac{7}{60}$	$\frac{31}{40}$	$\frac{4}{5}$	$\frac{3}{13}$

Oral and mental starter

- The students will need calculators.
- Using a target board like that shown on the right, ask the students if they can predict which of the fractions, when converted to a decimal, will terminate and which will recur.
- The students have met these ideas before but may need to be reminded of them.
- After they have made their predictions, ask them to work out the decimals on their calculators.
- These can then be written on the board and the recurring notation explained to the students. For example $\frac{4}{15} = 0.2\dot{6}$, $\frac{32}{33} = 0.\dot{9}\dot{6}$.
- Ask if there is any relationship between the denominators that give terminating decimals? They are all multiples of powers of 2 (2, 4, 8, 16, …), powers of 5 (5, 25, 125, …), powers of 10 (10, 100, 1000, …), or products of these such as 40 (4 × 10), 50 (5 × 10) … .

Main lesson activity

- This follows on from the Oral and mental starter.
- Ask the students: How would you write a recurring decimal as a fraction: for example, 0.454 545 … = 0.$\dot{4}\dot{5}$?
- Give them the chance to see whether they can find the answer by trial and improvement. They may find the answer of $\frac{5}{11}$.
- Outline the following method.

$$\begin{aligned} \text{Let} \qquad F &= 0.454\,545\,45 \,(1) \\ \text{Then} \qquad 100F &= 45.454\,545 \quad (2) \\ \text{Subtract } (2) - (1): \quad 99F &= 45 \\ \text{Divide by 99:} \qquad F &= \frac{45}{99} = \frac{5}{11} \quad \text{(Cancel by 9)} \end{aligned}$$

- Ask: Why multiply by 100?
- Establish that we have to multiply by the power of 10 equivalent to the number of recurring digits.
- Now repeat with 0.$\dot{7}$ ($\frac{7}{9}$), 0.$\dot{2}3\dot{4}$ ($\frac{26}{111}$).
- Ask: Can anyone see a connection or a short cut?
- Establish that when there is just one recurring digit, the denominator will be 9; when there are two recurring digits, the denominator will be 99; and when there are three recurring digits, the denominator will be 999.
- Be careful! This rule works only when the recurring digits are the only digits after the decimal point. It will not work with a number such as 0.377 777 7 … = 0.3$\dot{7}$. However, at this level, this is all that is needed. Other types of recurring decimal are a higher GCSE topic.
- Give some examples:
  $$0.\dot{6} = \frac{6}{9} = \frac{2}{3} \qquad 0.\dot{3}\dot{9} = \frac{39}{99} = \frac{13}{33} \qquad 0.\dot{6}7\dot{5} = \frac{675}{999} = \frac{25}{37}$$

- **The class can now do Exercise 7C from Pupil Book 2.**

Plenary

- Put this recurring decimal on the board: $0.277\,777\,77\ldots = 0.2\dot{7}$.
- Give the students a few moments to see whether they can find its fraction by trial and improvement.
- Now work through the procedure.

  Let $\qquad\qquad\quad F = 0.277\,777\,77\ldots$ (1)
  Multiply by 10: $\quad 10F = 2.777\,777\,77\ldots$ (2)
  Subtract (2) − (1): $\quad 9F = 2.5$
  Divide by 9: $\qquad\quad F = \frac{2.5}{9} = \frac{5}{18}$

- Repeat with $0.166\,66\ldots$ $(\frac{1}{6})$ and $0.416\,666\ldots$ $(\frac{5}{12})$

Homework

1 Write each of the following fractions as a recurring decimal.

   a $\frac{4}{7}$ **b** $\frac{85}{101}$ **c** $\frac{17}{33}$

2 Write each of the following recurring decimals as a fraction in its simplest form.

   a $0.\dot{5}\dot{4}$ **b** $0.\dot{2}4\dot{6}$ **c** $0.\dot{2}$ **d** $0.\dot{1}\dot{2}$

Answers
1 **a** $0.\dot{5}7142\dot{8}$ **b** $0.\dot{8}41\dot{5}$ **c** $0.5\dot{1}$
2 **a** $\frac{6}{11}$ **b** $\frac{82}{333}$ **c** $\frac{2}{9}$ **d** $\frac{4}{33}$

Framework objectives – Multiplying decimals

Use standard column procedures for multiplication of integers and decimals, including by decimals such as 0.6 or 0.06. Understand where to position the decimal point by considering equivalent calculations.

Oral and mental starter

- Prepare some cards with large whole numbers on them such as 200, 30, 4000.
- Produce two cards and ask the students to multiply the numbers together.
- Check the answers obtained by the students, then do another example.

Main lesson activity

- This is a revision lesson on multiplying decimals.
- Recall the rules for making calculations such as 0.3×0.05. Start with $3 \times 5 = 15$ and note that there are $0.\_ \times 0.\_\_ = 0.\_\_\_$ three **decimal places**, so the answer is 0.015.
- Give some examples, such as:
  $0.004 \times 0.03 (= 0.000\,12)$ $0.5 \times 0.007 (= 0.0035)$
- Recall the rules for making calculations such as 200×0.007. Rewrite as **equivalent products** until suitably simplified. For example:
  $$200 \times 0.007 = 20 \times 0.07$$
  $$= 2 \times 0.7 = 1.4$$
- Give some examples, such as:
  $$300 \times 0.07 = 30 \times 0.7$$
  $$= 3 \times 7 = 21$$
  $$40 \times 0.0008 = 4 \times 0.008 = 0.032$$
- Confirm the principle that, in the multiplication of two numbers, when one number is multiplied by 10, the other must be divided by 10.
- Now introduce a calculation such as 12.7×0.52.
- As the students may know a variety of ways to do long multiplication, they need to be shown at least three methods. These are the standard column method, the box method without decimals, and the box method with decimals.
- Whichever method students use, they should be encouraged to estimate the answer first. In the first two methods, they also have to work out how many decimal places there will be in the answer.

Column method

```
    127
 ×   52
    254
   6350
   6604
```

Box method 1

	100	20	7	Total
50	5000	1000	350	6350
2	200	40	14	254
			Total	6604

Box method 2

	10	2	0.7	Total
0.5	5	1.0	0.35	6.35
0.02	0.2	0.04	0.014	0.254
			Total	6.604

By all three methods the answer is 6.604.

- **The class can now do Exercise 7D from Pupil Book 2.**

Plenary

- Discuss the reason why we count in a base of 10 – probably because we have 10 fingers.
- Ask pupils to come up with as many words beginning with *dec-* that have a relation to 10.
- Some of these are decagon, decade, decimate, December, decahedron, decalitre, decalogue, decametre, decan, decapoda, decastyle, decasyllabic, decathalon, decennial, decile, decilitre, decimetre,

You could ask for pupils to find as many as possible before the next lesson.

Key Words

- decimal place
- product
- equivalent product

Homework

1 Without using a calculator, write down the answer to each of these.

  a 0.5×0.7 **b** 0.5×0.2 **c** 0.8×0.8 **d** 0.9×0.3

2 Without using a calculator, work out each of these.

  a 200×0.06 **b** 0.07×300 **c** 0.4×400 **d** 0.03×700

3 Without using a calculator, work out the answer to each of the following. Use any method you are happy with.

  a 63.5×0.42 **b** 1.35×1.7

Answers
  1 **a** 0.35 **b** 0.1 **c** 0.64 **d** 0.27
  2 **a** 12 **b** 21 **c** 160 **d** 21
  3 **a** 26.67 **b** 2.295

Framework objectives – Dividing decimals

Use standard column procedures for division of integers and decimals, including by decimals such as 0.6 or 0.06. Understand where to position the decimal point by considering equivalent calculations.

Oral and mental starter

- Prepare some cards with large whole numbers on them, such as 200, 30, 4000, and some cards with decimals on them, such as 0.3, 0.005, 0.04.
- Produce one card from each set and ask the students to multiply the numbers together.
- Check the answers obtained by the students, then do another example.

Main lesson activity

- This is a revision lesson on dividing integers and decimals.
- Remind the students of the rules used for making calculations such as $0.006 \div 0.2$. That is, rewrite them as **equivalent divisions**. For example:

  $0.006 \div 0.2 = 0.06 \div 2 = 0.03$
- Repeat the process with:

  $$0.4 \div 0.01 = 4 \div 0.1$$
  $$= 40 \div 1 = 40$$
  $$0.45 \div 0.009 = 4.5 \div 0.09$$
  $$= 45 \div 0.9$$
  $$= 450 \div 9 = 50$$
- Work through further examples covering a variety of calculations, such as:

  $$5000 \div 0.002 = 50\,000 \div 0.02$$
  $$= 500\,000 \div 0.2$$
  $$= 5\,000\,000 \div 2 = 2\,500\,000$$
  $$4.8 \div 300 = 0.48 \div 30$$
  $$= 0.048 \div 3 = 0.016$$
  $$0.38 \div 20 = 0.038 \div 2 = 0.019$$
  $$45 \div 3000 = 4.5 \div 300$$
  $$= 0.45 \div 30$$
  $$= 0.045 \div 3 = 0.015$$
- Confirm the principle that, in division involving two numbers, when one number is multiplied or divided by 10, the other must also be multiplied or divided by 10.
- Now introduce a calculation such as $7.02 \div 1.8$. First, estimate the answer: $7.02 \div 1.8 \approx 7 \div 2 = 3.5$. Then write as an equivalent problem without decimal points, $702 \div 18$, and use repeated subtraction (chunking). This gives:

  $$
  \begin{array}{r r l}
   & 702 & \\
  - & 360 & (20 \times 18) \\
  \hline
   & 342 & \\
  - & 180 & (10 \times 18) \\
  \hline
   & 162 & \\
  - & 90 & (5 \times 18) \\
  \hline
   & 72 & \\
  - & 72 & (4 \times 18) \\
  \hline
   & 0 & (39 \times 18) \\
  \end{array}
  $$

  Insert the decimal point, which gives $7.02 \div 1.8 = 3.9$.
- **The class can now do Exercise 7E from Pupil Book 2.**

Plenary

- This plenary covers both multiplication and division of decimals.
- Ask the students to give a number which makes 0.8 smaller when multiplied by that number.
- Obtain some examples and write them on the board. What is the common characteristic?
- Establish that multiplying by any value less than 1 makes 0.8 smaller.
- What about a number that makes 0.8 larger when multiplied by that number?
- Obtain some examples and write them on the board. What is the common characteristic?
- Establish that any value larger than 1 will work.
- Repeat the above procedures with 0.8 divided by a number.
- Establish that values greater than 1 make 0.8 smaller and values less than 1 make 0.8 larger.
- If time is available, test the students' understanding by asking for the missing values in:

$$0.8 \times \ldots = 8 \qquad 0.8 \div \ldots = 0.08 \qquad 0.8 \times \ldots = 0.08 \qquad 0.8 \div \ldots = 8$$

Key Words

- equivalent calculation
- decimal place

Homework

1 Without using a calculator, work out each of these.

   a $0.6 \div 0.03$ **b** $0.8 \div 0.2$ **c** $0.08 \div 0.1$ **d** $0.8 \div 0.04$

2 Without using a calculator, work out each of these.

   a $600 \div 0.6$ **b** $800 \div 0.2$ **c** $80 \div 0.08$ **d** $600 \div 0.02$

3 Without using a calculator, work out each of these.

   a $4.2 \div 20$ **b** $2.8 \div 400$ **c** $16 \div 400$ **d** $4.5 \div 90$

4 Without using a calculator, work out each of the following. Use any method you are happy with.

   a $9.36 \div 1.8$ **b** $6.76 \div 2.6$

Answers
 1 a 20 **b** 4 **c** 0.8 **d** 20
 2 a 1000 **b** 4000 **c** 1000 **d** 30 000
 3 a 0.21 **b** 0.007 **c** 0.04 **d** 0.05
 4 a 5.2 **b** 2.6

LESSON 7.6

Framework objectives – Efficient use of a calculator

Use a calculator efficiently and appropriately to perform complex calculations with numbers of any size, knowing not to round during intermediate steps of a calculation.

Use the constant, π and sign change keys, the function keys for powers, roots and fractions, brackets and the memory.

Oral and mental starter

- Due to the variety of calculators in use and the problems this may cause, there is no Oral and mental starter. However, some of the main keys listed in the Framework objectives could be discussed and found for the different makes of calculator. Some students may need help to locate the inverse/shift keys, which are needed on many calculators in order to do powers.

Main lesson activity

- This is a review lesson on the effective use of calculators.
- The students should have met most of the appropriate keys before.
- Do a variety of problems using the appropriate keys. Make sure the students can find these keys on their calculators.
- Work out, for example, $\sqrt{\pi} \div 5.3^2$. This requires the square root key, the π key and the square key. The answer is $0.334\,425\,254\,9 \approx 0.33$.
- Discuss the need to round answers to a sensible degree of accuracy.
- Now take 4.5^5. This requires the power key. The answer is $1845.281\,25 \approx 1845$.
- As the next example, work out:
$$\left(\tfrac{7}{8} - \tfrac{5}{12}\right) \div \left(\tfrac{11}{15} + \tfrac{7}{12}\right)$$
This requires the fraction key and the brackets keys. The answer is $\tfrac{55}{158}$.
- Finally, work out:
$$\frac{3.56(43.2 - 17.48)}{(4.53 - 1.2)\,0.92}$$
This requires the brackets keys. The answer is $29.887\,452\,67 \approx 29.89 \approx 30$.

- **The class can now do Exercise 7F from Pupil Book 2.**

Plenary

Key Words

- This is the last time that calculators will be the focus of the lesson, so each student needs to be sure that he/she can use his/her particular model. Make sure that they can identify the following keys: brackets, memory (M in, M+, M–), π, square root, square, power, fraction.
- This leaves only three principal keys that will be needed in future: sine, cosine and tangent.

☐ **fraction**
☐ **brackets**
☐ **square root**
☐ **square**
☐ **power**
☐ **pi**
☐ **memory keys**

Homework

1 Use a calculator to evaluate each of these.

   a $[2.4^2 + (6.7 - 1.04)]^2$ **b** $\dfrac{63.4 \times 21.02}{2.9(4.5 - 1.72)}$ **c** $\dfrac{19}{21} - \dfrac{7}{18}$

2 Use the power key to evaluate each of these.

   a 2.7^5 **b** $42.875^{\frac{2}{3}}$

Answers
   1 **a** 130.4164   **b** 165.3   **c** $\frac{65}{126}$
   2 **a** 143.5   **b** 12.25

LESSON 7.7

Framework objectives – Solving problems

Solve substantial problems by breaking them into simpler tasks, using a range of efficient techniques, methods and resources, including ICT.

Use trial and improvement where a more efficient method is not obvious.

Oral and mental starter

- Prepare several cards bearing numbers such as 0.01, 0.003, 0.05.
- Choose two cards and ask the students to multiply together the numbers on them.
- Check the students' answers then move on to a new problem.

Main lesson activity

- This lesson is on problem-solving strategies.
- Do some examples. One is given below and there is the question which opens the section in Pupil Book 2. (The better value is the small jar giving 510 grams per £1 as opposed to the large jar giving 500 grams per £1). Examples 7.17 and 7.18 could also be worked through.
- Some students may find it helpful for the strategies for each question in Exercise 7G to be discussed.
- In the grid below left, each square has to be filled in with a digit from 1 to 9, so that each total on a diagonal matches the given number for that diagonal.

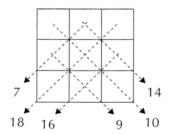

Answer:

1	5	8
2	6	9
4	7	3

There are other answers.

The strategy is to do the 16 diagonal first, as it must be 7 and 9. Then use trial and improvement for the rest.

- **The class can now do Exercise 7G from Pupil Book 2.**

Exercise 7G Answers

1 Adult £4.50, child £3.50
2 22 times (6 old pence is equivalent to 2.5 new pence)
3 Increase in sales is £1982 (to nearest £1), so the promotion probably was not worth while given its cost
4 **a** 14.3% ($\frac{1}{7}$)   **b** 50%   **c** 8.3% ($\frac{1}{12}$)
5 Tim 4 + 10 + 7 + 0 + 10 = 31 points, Tom 7 + 7 + 10 + 4 + 4 = 32 points; Tom wins
6 9 is last digit
7 33.88 = 33 jars
8 24 (42 = 1.75 × 24), 36 (63 = 1.75 × 36), 48 (84 = 1.75 × 48)
9 594 kg
10 59 hairs

SATs Answers

1 **a** 1.2 m   **b** 1.15 m   **c** 170 cm
2 **a** 91.44 m   **b** 109.36 yards
3 2.5, 0.1
4 **a** 9.2   **b** 30 × 38 = 1140
5 Using film of 24 photos costs £56.10. Using film of 36 photos costs £61.40. For 360 photos, 24 photo films are £5.30 cheaper.
6 **a** 0.636 62   **b** 0.528 68
7 $a = 1500$, $b = 20$
8 13 403.076 92, 13 000

Plenary

Key Words

- ☐ **strategy**
- ☐ **method**

● Discuss the strategies used to solve some of the problems in Exercise 7G.

Homework

Do not use a calculator for Question 2.

1 If you have already started the extension activity, complete the poster for homework, otherwise do the next two problems.

2 ● Choose a two-digit number such as 18. Multiply the units digit by 3 and add the tens digit. That is, $3 \times 8 + 1 = 25$.

   ● Repeat with the new number. That is, $3 \times 5 + 2 = 17$.

   ● Keep repeating the procedure until the numbers start repeating, namely:

   $$17 \longrightarrow 22 \longrightarrow 8 \longrightarrow 24 \longrightarrow \ldots$$

   ● Show the chains on a poster. For example:

3 Work out the chains for all the numbers up to 40.

Answers

2

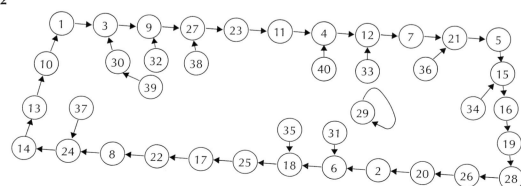

Algebra 4

Framework objectives – Factorisation
Use the prime factor decomposition of a number.

Oral and mental starter

- Ask if anyone has been to France or Germany recently. If they have, then ask how many euros they got for a pound.
- At the time of writing, there are approximately 1.50 (or $\frac{3}{2}$) euros to the pound. Hence, an easy way to check for comparison while shopping abroad is to divide the price in euros by 3, then double the result to give the approximate price in pounds.
- Go through a few examples, such as:

  25 euros: dividing by 3 gives about 8, doubling this gives 16, so 25 euros is about £16

  37 euros: divide by 3 gives about 12, double this gives 24, so 37 euros is about £24
- Now ask the students to try this themselves to convert the following euro prices to the approximate equivalent in pounds:

  9 euros (£6), 15 euros (£10), 22 euros (£14), 29 euros (£20), 49 euros (£32)

Main lesson activity

- This activity will recall factors and the HCF of number pairs, then introduce their use with algebraic expressions.
- Put on the board the number 6. Tell the class that this is a very interesting number and ask if anyone knows why. Tell them that 'it's not because this is the number of bowls in an over at cricket ' – or some other examples that are relevant to your students.
- The answer you are looking for is that 6 is the only number whose factors add up to itself, that is $1 + 2 + 3 = 6$.
- Now ask if anyone can explain what factors are.
- Establish with the class that factors are whole numbers that divide exactly into a given number, and that they always occur in pairs.
- Introduce the numbers 12 and 18. Ask the class if they can tell you what the common factors are, that is, which numbers divide exactly into both 12 and 18.
- You should be given the list: 1, 2, 3 and 6.
- Remind the class of the concept of the HCF (Highest Common Factor). In this case the HCF is 6, as 6 is the highest number that will divide exactly into both 12 and 18.
- You may need to go through a few more examples, such as:

  16 and 24: common factors are 1, 2, 4 and 8, HCF = 8

  30 and 45: common factors are 1, 3, 5 and 15, HCF = 15

  24 and 36: common factors are 1, 2, 3, 4, 6 and 12, HCF = 12
- Now introduce an algebraic expression, such as $5x$. What are the factors of $5x$?
- Go back to the earlier definition of factors as numbers which divide exactly into the given number. What divides exactly into $5x$? One answer is 5, so two factors of $5x$ are 5 and x. Point out that since an algebraic expression contains both numbers and letters, there will be both numbers and letters in the factors.
- Give another expression, such as $3a^2b$, what are the factors of this expression?
- Get the class to help you write a list of all the numbers and expressions that divide exactly into the expression. Again look for anything that divides exactly, that is:

  $1, 3, a, a^2, b, ab, a^2b, 3a, 3b, 3ab, 3a^2, 3a^2b$

  You will need to go through this breakdown very carefully, and even use a few more examples. You may want to write a second list in which each factor is paired with its partner.
- Now introduce the HCF of a pair of expressions, using say $6b$ and $9ab$. The common factors here are 3, b and $3b$, so the HCF is $3b$. You may want to write out a list of factors for each expression, in order to establish this firmly.
- Tell the class that in general the HCF of a pair of expressions can be found by the following method:
  ○ Find the HCF of their numbers.
  ○ Then find all the letters they have in common.

○ Finally, multiply together these two answers.

They will find it useful to write out a list of common factors when doing this.

● Go through another example of finding the HCF, such as with $6a^2b$ and $12ab^2$ (HCF = $6ab$).

● **The class can now do Exercise 8A from Pupil Book 2.**

Exercise 8A Answers

1 a 1, 2 **b** 1, 3 **c** 1, 5 **d** 1, 2
2 a 2 **b** 8 **c** 16 **d** 28
3 b $\frac{4}{7}$ **c** $\frac{2}{3}$ **d** $\frac{3}{5}$ **e** $\frac{3}{7}$
4 a i 1, a, b, ab **ii** ab **b i** 1, 5, c, $5c$ **ii** $5c$ **c i** 1, 2, h, $2h$ **ii** $2h$ **d i** 1, 2, a,
  $2a$ **ii** $2a$ **e i** 1, 2, 4, p, $2p$, $4p$ **ii** $4p$ **f i** 1, 5, m, p, $5m$, $5p$, mp, $5mp$ **ii** $5mp$
5 a i 1, a **ii** a **b i** 1, b **ii** b **c i** 1, 2, a, b, $2a$, $2b$, ab, $2ab$ **ii** $2ab$
  d i 1, 2, b, c, $2b$, $2c$, bc, $2bc$ **ii** $2bc$ **e i** 1, 3, m, n, $3m$, $3n$, mn, $3mn$ **ii** $3mn$
  f i 1, 2, 4, p, q, $2p$, $2q$, pq, $4p$, $4q$, $2pq$, $4pq$ **ii** $4pq$
6 a $2a$ **b** $3ab$ **c** $3ab$ **d** bc **e** $3mn$ **f** $2pq$

Extension Answers

1 $(10a + 1a) = a(10 + 1) = a \times 11$, which is a multiple of 11
2 $b = a + c$, so $100a + 10b + c = 100a + 10(a + c) + c$
  $= 100a + 10a + 10c + c$
  $= 110a + 11c$
  $= 11(10a + c)$, which is a multiple of 11

Plenary

● Ask the students for the HCF of $10x$ and $100x^2$.
● Discuss with the class the fact that you need the 10 as well as the x to give $10x$ as the highest common factor, even though this is one of the expressions itself. Compare with finding the HCF of 16 and 32.
● Give the class a HCF of say $3b$ and ask for which two expressions this could be the HCF.
● Possibilities include, $3ab$ and $3bc$, or $6ab^2$ and $9bdef$.

Key Words

☐ **factor**
☐ **common factor**
☐ **HCF**

Homework

1 Write down all the common factors of each of the following pairs of numbers.

  a 12 and 16 **b** 36 and 20 **c** 20 and 45 **d** 24 and 36

2 Write down the HCF of each of the following pairs of numbers.

  a 18 and 45 **b** 32 and 48 **c** 56 and 70 **d** 66 and 48

3 Find the HCF of the numerator and denominator in order to cancel down each of the following fractions.

  b $\frac{15}{25}$ **c** $\frac{36}{48}$ **d** $\frac{24}{40}$ **e** $\frac{16}{24}$

4 Write down **i** all the common factors of each pair of expressions and **ii** the HCF.

  a $4ab$ and $5ab$ **b** $2cd$ and $6c$ **c** $6gh$ and $8h$ **d** $5b^2c$ and $10bc$

  e $9m^2n^2$ and $12mn$ **f** $2p^2t$ and $6pt^2$

5 Write down the HCF of the following;

  a $6a^2$ and $8ap$ **b** $12ad^2$ and $9ad$ **c** $5a^2c$ and $10ac^2$ **d** $3bk^2$ and $9bk$

  e $10p^2t^2$ and $8pt$ **f** $12p^2w$ and $18pw^2$

Answers
1 a 1, 2, 4 **b** 1, 2, 4 **c** 1, 5 **d** 1, 2, 3, 4, 6, 12
2 a 9 **b** 16 **c** 14 **d** 6
3 b $\frac{3}{5}$ **c** $\frac{3}{4}$ **d** $\frac{3}{5}$ **e** $\frac{2}{3}$
4 a i 1, a, b, ab **ii** ab **b i** 1, 2, c, $2c$ **ii** $2c$ **c i** 1, 2, h, $2h$ **ii** $2h$ **d i** 1, 5, b, c, bc, $5b$, $5c$, $5bc$ **ii** $5bc$
  e i 1, 3, m, n, $3m$, $3n$, mn, $3mn$ **ii** $3mn$ **f i** 1, 2, p, t, $2p$, $2t$, pt, $2pt$ **ii** $2pt$
5 a $2a$ **b** $3ab$ **c** $5ac$ **d** $3bk$ **e** $2pt$ **f** $6pw$

Framework objectives – Index notation with algebra

Use index notation for integer powers and simple instances of the index laws.

Oral and mental starter

- Ask the class approximately how many litres there are to a gallon. The correct answer is about four and a half.
- Then ask how many litres there are in 8 gallons. The answer is 36.
- Ask the students how they arrived at this answer and discuss the various methods used.
- One way is to multiply the 4 by 8, getting 32, then to find the result of eight halves, which is 4. Then add the two together, giving 32 + 4 = 36.
- Now ask how many litres there are in:

    12 gallons = 54 litres; 22 gallons = 99 litres; 17 gallons = $76\frac{1}{2}$ litres.
- Now ask approximately how many gallons is 60 litres.
- Discuss the strategy. For an approximation, you would not try to divide by 4.5. Rather you would divide by 4 and also by 5 and go for a midway answer. Here this gives 60 ÷ 4 = 15 and 60 ÷ 5 = 12. Approximately halfway between 15 and 12 is 13.5 which is rounded up to 14.
- Ask the class how many gallons there are in:

    100 litres = 22 gallons; 70 litres = 16 gallons; 40 litres = 9 gallons;
    134 litres = 30 gallons.

Main lesson activity

- Explain to the class that they are going to look at the power of mathematics using small numbers.
- Write on the board $2 \times 2 \times 2 \times 2 \times 2 \times 2 \times 2 \times 2 \times 2 \times 2$. Ask the class what this sum represents – multiplying a 2 by itself ten times. Show that in mathematics this can be written more simply by using powers. Show them that the sum can be written as 2^{10}. Explain the terminology '2 to the power 10'.
- This would be a good time to show the class (or remind them) how to use the power keys on their calculators. The answer 1024 should be displayed on their calculators.
- Show how the same principle works with algebra, so that $k \times k \times k \times k \times k = k^5$.
- Now, write on the board $x^3 \times x^2$, and ask the class if they can tell you what the answer to this expression could be. If someone comes up with the correct answer of x^5, ask them to explain why.
- Explain that if each term is expanded, we get $(x \times x \times x) \times (x \times x)$ which becomes $x \times x \times x \times x \times x$, which in turn becomes x^5. Show how this way of calculating is carried out by simply adding the powers.
- Show a few more simple examples like the one above to illustrate that the following rule will always work:

    $x^a \times x^b = x^{a+b}$
- Write on the board the expression $m^8 \div m^5$ and ask if anyone can tell you what the answer should be. If someone comes up with the correct answer of m^3, ask them to explain why.
- The explanation is best shown like this:

    $$m^8 \div m^5 = \frac{m \times m \times m \times m \times m \times m \times m \times m}{m \times m \times m \times m \times m} = m \times m \times m = m^3$$
- Show a few more simple examples like the one above to illustrate that the following rule will always work:

    $x^a \div x^b = x^{a-b}$

- **The class can now do Exercise 8B from Pupil Book 2.**

Plenary

- Discuss with the class why we use powers – they shorten very big numbers and also make very small numbers accessible.
- Remind the class of the large number 10^{100}, called the Googol. Tell them that this was the answer to the million pound question on the television programme *Who Wants to be a Millionaire* when Major Charles Ingram was suspected of cheating.

Key Words

- [ ] power
- [ ] index

Homework

1 Expand the following, and find their value (use a calculator if necessary).

a 2^6 **b** 3^5 **c** 6^4 **d** 4^5 **e** 17^2 **f** 14^3 **g** 27^2 **h** 11^4

2 Write down the following in index form:

a $t \times t \times t \times t$ **b** $t \times t \times t \times t \times t \times t$ **c** $m \times m$ **d** $q \times q \times q$

3 **a** Write $m + m + m + m + m + m$ as briefly as possible.

b Write $t \times t \times t \times t \times t \times t$ as briefly as possible.

c Show the difference between $6m$ and m^6.

d Show the difference between t^4 and $4t$.

4 Write down the answer to each of the following in index form:

a $4^3 \times 4^4$ **b** $6^4 \times 6^5$ **c** $9^4 \times 9^3$ **d** $m^3 \times m^5$ **e** $p^4 \times p^4$ **f** $k^5 \times k^4$

Answers

1 **a** 64 **b** 243 **c** 1296 **d** 1024 **e** 289 **f** 2744 **g** 729 **h** 14641

2 **a** t^4 **b** t^5 **c** m^2 **d** q^3

3 **a** $6m$ **b** t^6 **c** $6m = m + m + m + m + m + m$, $m^6 = m \times m \times m \times m \times m \times m$
d $t^4 = t \times t \times t \times t$, $4t = t + t + t + t$

4 **a** 4^7 **b** 6^9 **c** 9^7 **d** m^8 **e** p^8 **f** k^9

Framework objectives – Square roots and cube roots

Estimate square roots and cube roots.

Oral and mental starter

- Tell the class that approximation is a valuable skill. It enables a quick check on calculations – maybe even to ensure that you have used the calculator correctly.
- For example, ask the class if they can estimate the answer to 41 672 divided by 8.
- Ask for quick approximations and write them up on the board. After a few, discuss with the class any strategy that they had to estimate a division by 8.
- One way is to halve the number, halve again, then halve again for the third time to complete the division.
- Doing this with 41 672 gives us the approximate sequence:
  $$41\,672 \rightarrow 20\,000 \rightarrow 10\,000 \rightarrow 5000$$
- Estimate the following (all divisions by 8):
  $$629\,537 \rightarrow 300\,000 \rightarrow 150\,000 \rightarrow 80\,000$$
  $$173\,492 \rightarrow 90\,000 \rightarrow 45\,000 \rightarrow 22\,000$$
  $$23\,774 \rightarrow 12\,000 \rightarrow 6000 \rightarrow 3000$$
  $$117\,008 \rightarrow 60\,000 \rightarrow 30\,000 \rightarrow 15\,000$$

Main lesson activity

- Ask the class what the square root of 25 is.
- If only the answer 5 is given, remind the class that −5 is also a square root of 25.
- Now ask the class to estimate the square root of 20. Put their suggestions on the board.
- Discuss with the class any answers that are obviously wrong, and how they know they are wrong. For example, the square root of 20 must be larger than 4 as $4 \times 4 = 16$ which is less than 20. Similarly, the square root of 20 must be less than 5.
- Hence we know that the square root of 20 must lie between 4 and 5. It looks halfway, so a good estimate will be 4.5.
- Ask the pupils to work out the correct answer using their calculators. You can use this as an opportunity to show pupils how they can find square roots on their own calculator.
- The calculator will show the square root of 20 to be 4.472135955. This rounds to 4.5 – the approximation was correct. Ensure that the class know the correct symbol, $\sqrt{\ }$, for square root.
- Ask the class what the cube root of 8 is. You will need to explain that the cube root is the number that gives 8 when multiplied by itself three times. In this example the answer is 2, written as $\sqrt[3]{8}$.
- Ask the class why they think that there are no negative answers to a cube root.
- Write on the board a few better-known cube roots: the cube root of 27 is 3; the cube root of 125 is 5 and the cube root of 1000 is 10. Discuss why the numbers have grown so quickly.

- **The class can now do Exercise 8C from Pupil Book 2.**

1 a 4   b 5   c 8   d 10   e 15
2 a $x = 3, x = -3$ b $x = 6, x = -6$ c $x = 7, x = -7$ d $x = 11, x = -11$
3 a $x^2 = 50 \div 2 = 25$, hence $x = 5$ and $x = -5$ b $x^2 = 36 \div 4 = 9$, hence $x = 3$ and $x = -3$
4 a 5.1   b 7.4   c 9.7   d 10.4   e 16.6
5 a 2   b 1   c 5   d 3   e 10   f –4   g –1   h –10   i 0.1   j 0.2
6 b i 4.4   ii 4.6   iii 3.6   iv 6.4   v 12.6
7 a $\sqrt[3]{50}$ b $\sqrt{30}$ c $\sqrt{20}$ d $\sqrt{35}$ e $\sqrt{15}$ f $\sqrt{40}$
8 b i 3.6   ii 1.7   iii 7.9   iv 6.3   v 9.1   c i 4.0   ii 1.9   iii 7.4   iv 6.8   v 9.5
9 a 33   b 19   c 42   d 34   e 44

Extension Answers

a Sometimes true, only for A = B = 0
b Always true
c Never true
d Always true

Plenary

Key Words
- square root
- cube root

- Ask the class which is the biggest, the square root of ten thousand or the cube root of a million.
- The answer is they are both the same, one hundred.
- Go through the better-known square roots and cube roots as a quick competition, seeing which set of students (row, column, table) remembers the most. Use the list of roots on Pupil Book page 124, but ensure that all students have their textbooks shut.

Homework

1 Estimate the square root of each of the following. Then use a calculator find the result to one decimal place and see how close you were.

a $\sqrt{46}$ b $\sqrt{31}$ c $\sqrt{74}$ d $\sqrt{129}$ e $\sqrt{215}$

2 Without a calculator, state the cube roots of each of the following numbers.

a 64   b 343   c 216   d 729   e 512

3 a Estimate the integer closest to the cube root of each of the following.

i 96   ii 110   iii 55   iv 297   v 3000

b Use a calculator to find the accurate value of the above. Give your answers to one decimal place.

4 State which, in each pair of numbers, is the larger.

a $\sqrt{20}, \sqrt[3]{55}$ b $\sqrt{28}, \sqrt[3]{149}$ c $\sqrt{18}, \sqrt[3]{79}$

5 Estimate the cube root of each of these numbers without a calculator.

a 15   b 61   c 400   d 150   e 850

6 Try to estimate the cube root of each of these numbers without using a calculator.

a 25 000   b 8000   c 57 000   d 41 000   e 83 000

Answers
1 a 6.8   b 5.6   c 8.6   d 11.4   e 14.7
2 a 4   b 7   c 6   d 9   e 8
3 i 4.6   ii 4.8   iii 3.8   iv 6.7   v 14.4
4 a $\sqrt{20}$ b $\sqrt[3]{149}$ c $\sqrt[3]{79}$
5 a 2.5   b 3.9   c 7.4   d 5.3   e 9.5
6 a 29   b 20   c 38   d 34   e 44

Framework objectives – Constructing graphs involving time
Construct and interpret graphs arising from real situations.

Oral and mental starter

- Ask the class who can tell you the square root of 400.
- After some guesses, someone may come up with the correct answer of 20. Ask them how they worked it out.
- The quick way of getting to the solution is to recognise that $400 = 4 \times 100$. We know the square root of each of these numbers which gives the answer $2 \times 10 = 20$.
- Ask for the square root of 900. The correct answer of 30 should now be more forthcoming, but may still cause discussion before everyone sees the reasoning.
- Continue in this way, asking for square roots of:
  $1600 \to 40$; $4900 \to 70$; $12\,100 \to 110$; $810\,000 \to 900$; $90\,000 \to 300$
- Now ask if anyone can estimate the square root of 377.
- Let the question provoke discussion in the class with different suggestions being put on the board. If the correct answer of 19 is offered, ask how they worked the answer out.
- Explain that you can break down the number as 3.77×100. The square root of 100 we know is 10 and the square root of 3.77 can be estimated at between 1 and 2, but quite close to 2. The approximation 1.9 is quite reasonable, giving the root as $1.9 \times 10 = 19$.
- Repeat with other examples such as:
  $805 \to 28$; $548 \to 23$; $971 \to 31$; $457 \to 21$

Main lesson activity

- Draw a pair of axes labelled time on the horizontal axis and distance on the vertical axis on the board.
- Ask the students to tell you what a graph would look like representing a car travelling at a constant speed of 50 miles per hour.
- You should get the response 'straight line'. Draw this straight line and then ask if anyone can tell you a coordinate of any points on this line.
- Using the fact that the speed is 50 miles per hour, you could get answers from (0,0), (1,50), (2,100), (3,150) etc. Plot a few of these points on the graph.
- Now put another pair of axes on the board with the same labels.
- Ask the students to tell you what the graph would look like representing a car setting off from a standing start and accelerating up to 50 miles per hour.
- This time the response should be some sort of a curve, where the distance covered in the first few seconds is small, but then gradually increases as the speed increases. The curve should rise quickly and then straighten out into a straight line representing the steady 50 mph.
- Ask the class if they can give you any coordinates. The only certain coordinate they can give is (0,0). Any other points may be plausible and worth discussion.
- Draw another pair of axes labelled time on the horizontal axis and temperature on the vertical axis.
- Ask for the graph that represents the temperature of water in a boiling kettle, starting with cold water, the water heating up and then cooling down after it has boiled.
- You may need to deal with this in three parts. Boiling, with a curve, similar to the accelerating car, up to 100°C. Then a straight line and then a gradual curve coming down as the water loses heat.
- **The class can now do Exercise 8D from Pupil Book 2.**

Extension Answers

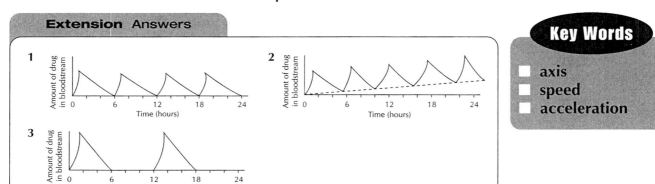

Key Words
- axis
- speed
- acceleration

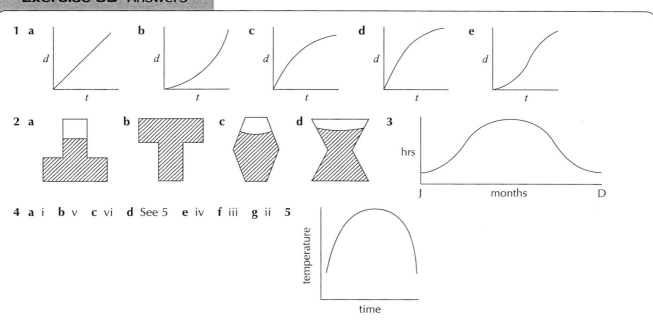

1 a d / t **b** d / t **c** d / t **d** d / t **e** d / t

2 a **b** **c** **d** **3** hrs / J months D

4 a i **b** v **c** vi **d** See 5 **e** iv **f** iii **g** ii **5** temperature / time

Plenary

- Draw a pair of distance–time axes on the board. Now draw a straight, horizontal line on the axes and ask the pupils what this might represent.
- Discuss with the class that this graph represents someone or something staying still.
- Now put on the board a pair of axes labelled speed on the vertical axis and time on the horizontal axis.
- Ask what the graph would look like if it were to represent a constant speed.
- The graph would again be a straight, horizontal line.
- Discuss what shape the graph might be if it represented acceleration. Explain that the graph could be horizontal or curved depending on whether it represented constant acceleration or a change in acceleration.

Homework

Draw sketch graphs to illustrate the following:

1 Distance travelled by a train accelerating away from a railway station.

2 The height of a parachutist jumping out of a plane and then pulling her ripcord to slow the descent.

3 The temperature inside a freezer when someone has left the freezer door wide open.

4 The number of people left in Old Trafford stadium after the final minute of a big game with all the gates open.

5 The population of the world since the year 2000 BC.

Answers

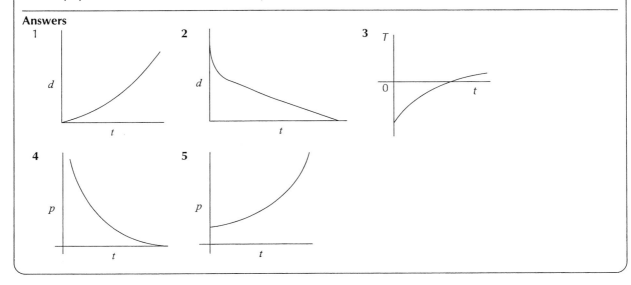

Handling Data 2

Framework objectives – Probability statements
Use the vocabulary of probability in interpreting results involving uncertainty and prediction.

Oral and mental starter

- Use a counting stick as a probability scale.

0   1

- Explain to the class that the stick is a probability scale. Tell them that one end is zero. Ask them for the value of the other end.
- Now point at the centre of the stick and ask them to tell you an event which has a probability of 0.5. (For example, obtaining a Head on a fair coin.)
- Now say to the class that you will point out a probability of something that happens and they will have to show you the probability that it does not happen. For example, you point to 0.1 on the stick, the class would point to 0.9. Repeat this quickly for different values.
- Finish by asking why 'Event happens' and 'Event does not happen' is not always at 0.5 (as there are two choices). Ask the class to give you examples to explain the reason, such as dice $P(6) = \frac{1}{6}$, $P(\text{not } 6) = \frac{5}{6}$.

Main lesson activity

- Remind the class that they should be able to find the probability of a range of situations, all of which they have already met. Draw their attention to the tabular summaries in Pupil Book 2.
- Move on to a brief discussion of **independent events**, giving them this definition:
    Two events are said to be independent when the outcome of one of them does not affect the outcome of the other event.
- Tell the class that most of the combined events they have dealt with so far have been independent:
    Give as an example a dice being rolled at the same time as a coin is tossed. Ask them whether they think that the score on the dice may affect how the coin lands – Heads or Tails.
- Two other aims of this lesson are to give students an understanding of when statements can be misleading even though they have apparently been deduced logically, and to increase their familiarity with the vocabulary of probability.
- Write on the board $a = b$ and $b = c$. Ask the class to give you an equation connecting a and c. They should respond $a = c$.
- Now replace the statements with the following sentence.
    Amy likes Bob and Bob likes chips.
  Ask the class to give you a statement connecting Amy and chips! Hopefully, the class will realise that the logic here does not necessarily work.
- Explain that sometimes statements may seem logical but are not necessarily true.
- Tell the class that you have five names on five separate pieces of paper, four boys and one girl. Ask them which statement is true when one piece of paper is picked at random.
    ○ There is an even chance of picking the girl because there are both boys and girls (meaning there are two choices).
    ○ There is no chance of picking the girl because she is outnumbered.
    ○ The probability of picking the girl is one fifth because there is a one in five chance.
- Explain to the class that these are the sort of statements they will have to consider. Their answers will require an explanation, not just responses such as 'It is incorrect'. Their explanations could include what the true statements should be.

- **The class can now do Exercise 9A from Pupil Book 2.**

1 a Probability of rolling 6 on a fair dice is $\frac{1}{6}$. The fact that Ashad thinks he is unlucky does not affect his chance of starting the game.
  b If this were true, it would rain forever.
  c Probability of snow depends which part of the world you are in and at what time of year.
  d Only true if there were equal numbers of mint, chocolate and plain sweets.
2 a Incorrect, it could happen today.
  b Correct, assuming it is a fair coin.
  c Incorrect, it is possible that the bus could be late tomorrow.
  d Incorrect, there is an equal chance of picking out red or blue.
3 a Not possible to know, as number of winning squares not given for each case.
  b Grid 1
  c Proportion of winning squares is Grid 1 $\frac{1}{4}$, Grid 2 $\frac{1}{3}$, Grid 3 $\frac{1}{2}$. So, greatest chance of winning is using Grid 3.
4 a Not independent because when Jonathon writes computer programs he is unlikely to be watching TV at the same time.
  b Independent **c** Independent

Extension Answers

5 by 5 grid with 7 winning squares has a probability of $\frac{7}{25}$ (0.28) to produce a winning square
6 by 6 grid with 10 winning squares has a probability of $\frac{10}{36}$ (0.27) to produce a winning square
10 by 10 grid with 27 winning squares has a probability of $\frac{27}{100}$ (0.27) to produce a winning square
Greatest chance of finding a winning square is on 5 by 5 grid.

Plenary

Key Words

- Ask the class to think of different sentences which have some logic to them but that are incorrect. (You could give them a hint by asking for a sentence about, for example, eye colour or shoe size.)
- Prompt them with an example of your own, such as:
  'There is a 50% chance that Jon is wearing size 10 shoes because either he is size 10 or he isn't.'
- Ask a student to explain why the statement is incorrect.

☐ **certain**
☐ **possibly**
☐ **even chance**
☐ **never**
☐ **probability**
☐ **probable**

Homework

1 Write down a reason why each of these statements is incorrect.
  a A bag contains black and white cubes, so there is a 50% chance of picking a black cube.
  b A bag contains black and white cubes. Last time I picked out a black cube, so this time I will pick out a white cube.
  c A bag contains one black cube and many white cubes. So, I have no chance of picking out the black cube.

2 Here are three different bags of cubes:
    A There are four black cubes and four white cubes in a bag.
    B There are two black cubes and five white cubes in a bag.
    C There are seven black cubes and five white cubes in the bag.
  Here are three statements about the bags of cubes:
    X There is a probability of $\frac{2}{5}$ that I will pick a black cube.
    Y There is an even chance that I will pick a black cube.
    Z There is a probability of $\frac{5}{12}$ that I will pick a white cube.
  For each bag, say whether the statements are correct or incorrect.

Answers
  1 a This would only be correct if there were an equal number of black and white cubes.
    b Provided there are still some black cubes in the bag, there is a chance that black might be picked out.
    c As in part **b**, there is a chance. It would only be impossible if the black cube had been taken from the bag.
  2 I Incorrect, C Correct

	A	B	C
X	I	I	I
Y	C	I	I
Z	I	I	C

Framework objectives – Mutually exclusive events and exhaustive events

Identify all the mutually exclusive outcomes of an experiment. Know that the sum of probabilities of all mutually exclusive outcomes is 1 and use this when solving problems.

Use efficient methods to add, subtract, multiply and divide fractions.

Oral and mental starter

- Use a target board as shown.
- Ask the class to pick out fractions and decimals which add up to one. Encourage them to give additions which involve more than two fractions/decimals:
  for example, $0.5 + 0.125 + \frac{3}{8}$.

$\frac{1}{2}$	0.25	$\frac{1}{4}$	0.85	$\frac{1}{8}$
0.15	$\frac{3}{4}$	0.125	$\frac{5}{8}$	0.625
$\frac{7}{8}$	0.1	$\frac{3}{8}$	0.5	0.75

- Ask them how they worked it out when they mixed fractions with decimals.
- Now give them one value and ask them to make it add up to 1, with two other fractions or decimals. They may use either the target board values or their own. For example: you say 0.2 and they give $0.5 + 0.3$.

Main lesson activity

- Give the class the example of a bag which contains three blue, two yellow and five green balls, from which only one ball is allowed to be picked at random. The probabilities for picking each colour are:

  $P(\text{blue}) = \frac{3}{10}$

  $P(\text{yellow}) = \frac{2}{10} = \frac{1}{5}$

  $P(\text{green}) = \frac{5}{10} = \frac{1}{2}$

  The events 'picking a blue ball', 'picking a yellow ball' and 'picking a green ball' can never happen at the same time, given that only one ball is allowed to be taken out. Such events are call mutually exclusive, because they do not overlap.

- Using the same example, deal with the probability of an event which will not happen. Thus, the probability of not picking out a blue ball is give by:

  $P(\text{not blue}) = \frac{7}{10}$

  because there are seven outcomes which are not blue balls. Then note that

  $P(\text{blue}) + P(\text{not blue}) = \frac{3}{10} + \frac{7}{10} = 1$

  So, knowing P(Event happening), then

  P(Event not happening) = 1 − P(Event happening)

- Now ask the class to sum the probabilities of picking the three coloured balls. Hopefully, they will get the correct answer – 1. Then tell them that because there are no other possibilities, they are called **exhaustive events**.

- Tell them that the events are also mutually exclusive and that when events are both exhaustive and mutually exclusive, the probabilities always **add up to 1**.

- **The class can now do Exercise 9B from Pupil Book 2.**

Key Words

- mutually
- exclusive
- exhaustive
- probability
- expectation

Plenary

- Tell the class that in a box you have a set of mathematical instruments and other equipment: for example, pens, pencils, pairs of compasses, protractors, and small and large rulers.
- You say that in one hand you have, for example, pencils, and in the other hand you have rulers. The class have to tell you whether the content of your hands is exhaustive, mutually exclusive or neither.
- Repeat this with different combinations.

Homework

1 Ten pictures are shown, which are all face down. A picture is picked at random.

   a What is the probability of choosing a picture of a guitar?

   b What is the probability of choosing a picture of a guitar or a boat?

   c What is the probability of choosing a picture of a horse or a doll?

   d What is the probability of choosing a picture which is not of a boat?

2 A bag contains a large number of discs, each labelled either A, B, C or D. The probabilities that a disc picked at random will have a given letter are shown below.

   P(A) = 0.2   P(B) = 0.4   P(C) = 0.15   P(D) = ?

   a What is the probability of choosing a disc with a letter D on it?

   b What is the probability of choosing a disc with a letter A or B on it?

   c What is the probability of choosing a disc which does not have the letter C on it?

Answers
 1 **a** $\frac{3}{10}$ **b** $\frac{7}{10}$ **c** $\frac{3}{10}$ **d** $\frac{3}{5}$
 2 **a** 0.25   **b** 0.6   **c** 0.85

Framework objectives – Estimates of probability

Estimate probabilities from experimental data.

Understand relative frequency as an estimate of probability and use this to compare outcomes of experiments.

Oral and mental starter

- Tell the class that in a test someone scored 7 out of 10. Ask a student to give you the score as a fraction of 10 (the way that teachers write the score on the test $\frac{7}{10}$). Ask another student to give you this score as a decimal.
- Repeat this for other simple scores, leading to, for example, $\frac{9}{10}$, $\frac{4}{10}$, $\frac{24}{100}$ and $\frac{32}{50}$.
- Gradually increase the level of difficulty up to scores which will need rounding: for example, 20 out of 30. Encourage the students to round to two decimal places.
- Finally, ask them to work out mentally simple fractions of quantities: for example, $\frac{7}{10}$ of 100, $\frac{2}{5}$ of 20.

Main lesson activity

- The aim is to recall the work on experimental probability, to introduce the term **relative frequency** and to move on to **expectation**.
- Ask the class to consider a coin which is tossed ten times and lands on Heads nine times. Ask them whether the coin is biased. They will probably say that it is.
- Now suggest that when the coin is tossed a further ten times, it landed on Heads only once. Ask the class whether they still think that it is biased. They will probably say that you cannot tell.
- Ask the class how they could improve the experiment. Hopefully, they will tell you to carry out more trials.
- Tell them that relative frequency is about carrying out repeated trials and obtaining estimates of probability from experimental data.
- Write down on the board the formula

$$\text{Relative frequency} = \frac{\text{Number of successful trials}}{\text{Total number of trials}}$$

- Emphasise that the greater the number of trials, the closer the estimates of probability get to the theoretical probability.
- Now say to the class that an experiment has been carried out many times and you believe that the estimate is reliable. For example, the coin landed on Heads 70 times out of 100, so the relative frequency is $\frac{70}{100}$. Ask them how many times they would expect this coin to land on Heads were it tossed 200 times. Stress that you are using the estimate of probability and not the theoretical probability.
- Then tell them that the expected number of successes can be calculated using the formula:

$$\text{Expected number of successes} = \text{Relative frequency} \times \text{Number of trials}$$

- **The class can now do Exercise 9C from Pupil Book 2.**

Exercise 9C Answers

1 a $\frac{32}{100}$ **b** Yes, it is probably biased: more 4s than other scores   **c** 160 (32 × 5)

2 a

Number on throws	10	20	30	40	50
Number of times it lands point up	6	13	20	24	32
Relative frequency of landing point up	0.6	0.65	0.67	0.6	0.64

b 0.64   **c** 0.64 × 200 = 128

3 a

Number of trials	10	25	50	100
Number of times blue cube chosen	3	8	15	28
Relative frequency	0.3	0.32	0.3	0.28

b 0.28   **c** 0.28 × 75 = 21

Plenary

Key Words

- Refer to the question in the extension work, which involves taking relative frequency from a graph.
- Explain to the class that relative frequency questions can be asked using experimental data either collected in a table or presented as a graph. Point out that the relative frequency plots can be read from a graph and that the number of successful trials can be calculated by working backwards.
- Discuss briefly why it is not possible to read values at intermediate points on a graph.

- relative
- frequency
- estimate
- probability
- expectation
- limit

Homework

A spinner has different coloured sections. It is spun 100 times and the number of times it lands on blue is recorded at regular intervals. The results are shown in the table.

Number of spins	20	40	60	80	100
Number of times lands on blue	6	10	15	22	26
Relative frequency	0.3				

a Copy and complete the table.

b What is the best estimate of the probability of landing on blue?

c How many times would you expect the spinner to land on blue in 2000 spins?

d If there are two sections of the spinner coloured blue, how many sections do you think there are altogether? Explain your answer.

Answers

a
Number of spins	20	40	60	80	100
Number of times lands on blue	6	10	15	22	26
Relative frequency	0.3	0.25	0.25	0.275	0.26

b 0.26   c 0.26 × 2000 = 520
d Assuming spinner is fair, 0.26 is close to $\frac{1}{4}$, so a quarter of the sections are blue. Hence, altogether there are eight sections.

CHAPTER 10

Shape, Space and Measures 3

> **Framework objectives** – Enlargements
>
> Enlarge 2-D shapes, given a centre of enlargement and a whole-number, a fractional or a negative scale factor, on paper and using ICT.
>
> Identify the scale factor of an enlargement as the ratio of the lengths of any two corresponding line segments.
>
> Recognise that enlargements preserve angle but not length, and understand the implications of enlargement for perimeter.

Oral and mental starter

- Imagine a cube which has an edge length of 2 cm. What is the volume of the cube? (Answer: 8 cm³)
- Now imagine the cube is twice as big. What is its volume now? (Answer: 64 cm³)
- Make sure that the students appreciate that 'twice as big' means that the edges of the cube are multiplied by two.
- This starter can be extended by asking the class to make the original cube three times or four times larger and allowing them to work out their answers on paper.

Main lesson activity

- Remind the class about **enlargement**, which was covered in Year 8.
- It may be necessary to revise enlargement, using the ray method, by drawing on the board the diagram shown on right, or show a prepared OHT.

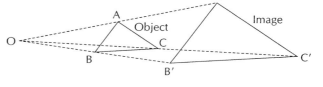

- State that the **object** triangle ABC has been enlarged by a **scale factor** of 2 about the **centre of enlargement**, O, to give the **image** triangle A'B'C'. The dashed lines are called the **rays** or **guidelines** for the enlargement. The object and image are on the *same side* of O. The scale factor is positive. This is called **positive enlargement**.
- Next, explain to the class that there is **fractional enlargement**.
- Draw on the board the diagram shown on right, or show a prepared OHT.

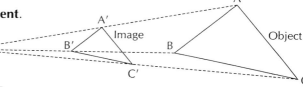

- Explain that each side of ΔA'B'C' is half the length of the corresponding side of ΔABC. Also that OA' = ½ of OA, OB' = ½ of OB and OC' = ½ of OC.
- That is, ΔABC has been enlarged by a scale factor of ½ about the centre of enlargement, O, to give the image ΔA'B'C'. The object and the image are on the *same side* of O, with the image *smaller* than the object. The scale factor is a fraction. This is called **fractional enlargement**.
- Then explain to the class that there is also **negative enlargement**. In this case, the image is *inverted* and on the *other side* of the centre of enlargement to the object. The scale factor is negative.
- Draw on the board (or have a prepared OHT) the diagram shown on right.
- Show the class that the lengths of the lines on flag B are double those on flag A.
- Also show them that the lengths of the rays from O to flag B are double those from O to flag A.
- Then state that object flag A has been enlarged by a scale factor of –2 about the centre of enlargement O to give image flag B.

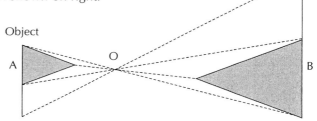

- Summarise the method for negative enlargement:
  ○ Draw rays from points on the object to O.
  ○ Measure the lengths of the rays and multiply these by the scale factor.
  ○ Continue the rays beyond O by these new lengths to find the corresponding points on the image.
  ○ Join these points to produce the image.
- Point out that, under any enlargement, corresponding angles on the object and image remain the same.
- Now demonstrate negative enlargement on a grid. Explain that the grid may or may not have coordinate axes x and y.
- Show the class how the image points can be easily found by counting grid units in the vertical and horizontal directions. This can be an alternative to drawing rays.
- When there are coordinate axes, the centre of enlargement is sometimes given as the origin (0, 0). The coordinates of the image shape are then the coordinates of the object shape multiplied by the negative scale factor.

- **The class can now do Exercise 10A from Pupil Book 2.**

Exercise 10A Answers

3 **a** Vertices at (−2, −2), (−6, −2), (−6, −6) **b** Vertices at (−2, −0), (−2, −4), (−6, −4), (−6, −0) **c** Vertices at (6, 0), (3, 4.5), (6, 9), (9, 4.5)
4 **a** −2 **b** (4, 8) **c** Rotation of 180° about (4, 8), then enlargement of scale factor 2 about (4, 8)
5 **b** A′(11, 2), B′(3, 2), C′(3, 6), D′(11, 6) **c i** 4 cm, 8 cm **ii** 1 : 2
   d i 12 cm, 24 cm **ii** 1 : 2 **e i** 8 cm², 32 cm² **ii** 1 : 4

Key Words

☐ **object**
☐ **image**
☐ **centre of enlargement**
☐ **scale factor**
☐ **negative enlargement**
☐ **negative scale factor**
☐ **fractional scale factor**

Plenary

- Ask what the class knows about each of these when making enlargements.
  ○ The relationship between lengths on the image and lengths on the object.
  ○ The relationship between angles on the image and angles on the object.
  ○ Fractional scale factor (makes a shape smaller on the same side of the centre of enlargement).
  ○ Positive scale factor.
  ○ Negative scale factor.

Homework

1 Draw copies of (or trace) each of the following shapes. Enlarge each one by the given scale factor about the centre of enlargement O.

   a Scale factor $\frac{1}{3}$

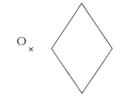

   b Scale factor −2

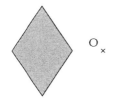

2 Copy each of the following shapes onto a coordinate grid and enlarge each one by scale factor −2 about the origin (0, 0).

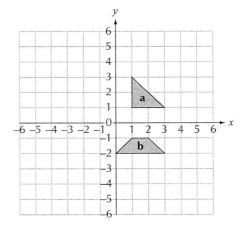

Answers
2 **a** Vertices at (−2, −2), (−6, −2), (−2, −6)
   b Vertices at (−2, 2), (−4, 2), (−6, 4), (0, 4)

Framework objectives – Planes of symmetry

Identify reflection symmetry in 3-D shapes.

Oral and mental starter

- To make sure that students can visualise common 3-D shapes from an oral description of plans and elevations, proceed as follows.
- Ask them to identify and write down, on their white-boards or in their books, the name of each of the following 3-D shapes. Check their answers after each oral description.
  - ⊙ Front and side elevation and the plan are all squares. (Answer: a cube)
  - ○ Front and side elevation are both triangles and the plan is a square. (Answer: a square-based pyramid)
  - ○ Front elevation is a rectangle, side elevation is a triangle and the plan is a rectangle. (Answer: a triangular prism)
  - ○ Front and side elevation and the plan are all equilateral triangles. (Answer: a tetrahedron)
  - ○ Front and side elevation and the plan are all circles. (Answer: a sphere)
- To help the students to visualise the shapes, show them models at the end of the starter.

Main lesson activity

- Tell the class that the lesson is about identifying the symmetry of 3-D shapes.
- Explain that a **plane** is a flat surface. That is, it is two dimensional.
- Remind them that all the 2-D shapes they have met so far may have one or more **lines** of **symmetry**.
- Now state that 3-D shapes may have one or more **planes of symmetry**. A plane of symmetry divides a 3-D shape into two identical parts, or halves. Each part is a reflection of the other in the plane of symmetry.
- On the board, or, using a prepared OHT, show the class the three different planes of symmetry for a cuboid. The three planes of symmetry are rectangles.

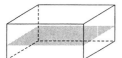  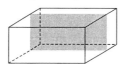

- Explain that if a mirror were to be placed on each of the planes of symmetry, the complete cuboid would be seen.
- Now name and pass around models of different of 3-D shapes for students to see and handle.
- Ask them to think about the different ways in which each can be divided to give two identical parts.

- **The class can now do Exercise 10B from Pupil Book 2.**

Exercise 10B Answers

1 **a** 5 **b** 9 **c** 6 **d** 4 **e** 9
2 **a** 4 **b** 7 **c** 9
3 $n + 1$
4 **a** 2 **b** 2 **c** 2
5 For example: cereal packet (3), chair (1), spoon (1), matchbox tray (2), pair of glasses (1), ball (infinite)
6 **a** 5 **b** 5 **c** 2 **d** 1 **e** 1 **f** 0 **g** 1 **h** 0

Extension Answers

1

2 **a** 2 for both
b 13 altogether: 3 from centre of face to centre of opposite face; 6 from centre of edge to centre of opposite edge; 4 from corner to diagonally opposite vertex

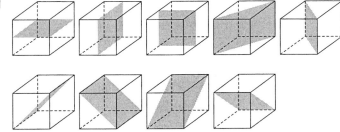

Plenary

- Again show the class various 3-D shapes used in the lesson.
- Ask them to write down the name of each one.
- Ask individual students to state the number of planes of symmetry for each one.

Key Words

- plane
- solid
- plane of symmetry
- axis of symmetry

Homework

1 Write down the number of planes of symmetry for each of the following 3-D shapes:

a

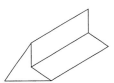

b

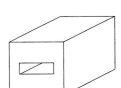

c

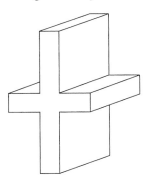

2 How many planes of symmetry does a cylinder have?

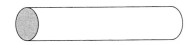

Answers
1 **a** 2 **b** 3 **c** 3
2 Infinite number

Framework objectives – Map scales

Use and interpret maps and scale drawings. Interpret and use ratio in a range of contexts.

Oral and mental starter

- On the board draw the table below, or use a prepared OHT.

1:10	1:8	1:12	2:80	1:4
8:200	1:2	20:720	1:5	8:800
1:20	10:300	5:50	1:36	5:25
1:40	20:80	1:30	100:800	10:500
40:80	4:48	1:100	10:200	1:25

- Ask individual students to cross out the pairs of ratios that are identical.
- The last student asked should then simplify the remaining ratio.

Main lesson activity

- Explain to the class that **maps** are two-dimensional **scale drawings** used to represent either local areas of land or geographical regions. Show the class various maps, drawing their attention to the different **map scales** which are used.
- Now show them a map with a scale of, say, 1 cm to 10 km. Explain how to work out the actual direct distance between two places on the map. For example, if the direct distance between A and B on a map is 4 cm, and the scale is 1 cm to 10 km, then the actual direct distance on the ground between A and B is 4 × 10 km = 40 km.
- Next, introduce the class to **map ratio** – the alternative to a map scale. A map ratio is the ratio of a distance on the map to the actual distance it represents on the ground. Map ratios are given in the form $1:x$ and have no units. A map ratio is also known as a **scale factor**.
- For example, say the map scale is 1 cm to 5 km. Now 1 km is 100 × 1000 cm. So the scale is 1 cm to 500 000 cm. Hence, the map ratio would be 1 : 500 000.
- Explain that when a more accurate distance than the direct distance is required, fine string may be used to measure distance on the map. Give as an example the use of an Ordnance Survey map to plan a walk.

- **The class can now do Exercise 10C from Pupil Book 2.**

- It is useful to have various maps of Great Britain available for the extension work, which show the different map scales used.

Plenary

● Ask the class to explain the two ways of representing distance on a map.
● Ask individual students to change various map scales to map ratios. For example: 1 cm to 100 m, 1 cm to 2 km, 1 cm to 50 km (respectively 1:10 000, 1:200 000, 1:5 000 000).

Key Words

- [ ] map
- [ ] scale drawing
- [ ] map scale
- [ ] map ratio
- [ ] scale factor

Homework

1 Write each of the following scales as a map ratio.

   a 1 cm to 2 m   **b** 1 cm to 7 m   **c** 4 cm to 1m

   d 1 cm to 10 km   **e** 1 cm to 400 km

2 A map ratio is 1:250 000. The direct distance between two towns is 18 cm on a map. What is the actual direct distance between the two towns?

3 The map shows eight towns in the Midlands. Find the *direct* distance between the following towns.

   a Birmingham and Coventry   **b** Stafford and Derby

   c Coventry and Stoke-on-Trent   **d** Birmingham and Nottingham

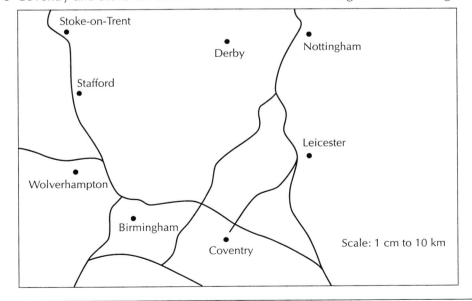

Scale: 1 cm to 10 km

Answers
  1 a 1:200 **b** 1:700 **c** 1:25 **d** 1:1 000 000 **e** 1:40 000 000
  2 45 km
  3 a 25 km **b** 40 km **c** 67 km **d** 66 km

Oral and mental starter

- Ask the class how to recognise congruent shapes. Their answer should be: 'Two shapes are congruent when they are exactly the same shape and size'.
- Draw on the board the following triangles, or use a prepared OHT.

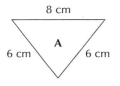
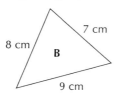
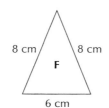
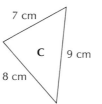
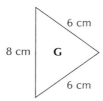

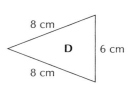
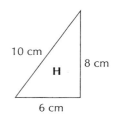

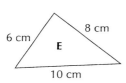

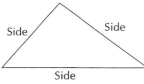
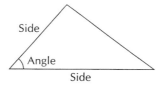
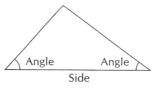
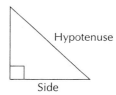

- Ask the class which pairs of triangles are congruent, inviting individual students to explain their answers.
- The following questions could also be asked:
  - ○ Do you need dimensions to show that the triangles are congruent?
  - ○ Do you have to draw the triangles exactly to prove that they are congruent?
  - ○ Do you need to be given any angles to show that the triangles are congruent?
- Ask them whether they can draw other pairs of triangles which are congruent but include angles.

Main lesson activity

- Tell the class that the lesson will show them how to prove that two triangles are congruent when information is given on both triangles.
- Remind the class that they already know how to construct triangles from given information, and summarise the following on the board or using an OHT.

Side / Side \ Side	Side \ Angle / Side	Angle / Angle \ Side	Hypotenuse / Side
Three sides (SSS)	Two sides and the included angle (SAS)	Two angles and the included side (ASA)	Right angle, hypotenuse and side (RHS)

- Now apply these conditions to show that the two triangles given on the right are congruent.
  Invite individual students to state which angles and which sides are equal. Write their responses on the board, which should be as follows:
  $\angle B = \angle X$
  $\angle C = \angle Y$
  $BC = XY$
  Then ask the class whether this proves that △ABC is congruent to △XYZ to which they should respond affirmatively. Get them to state the condition of congruency (ASA).
- Explain to the class that it is a convention to show congruency by using the symbol '≡'. Hence, the congruency of these two triangles may be written as:
  $\triangle ABC \equiv \triangle XYZ$
- **The class can now do Exercise 10D from Pupil Book 2.**

108 © HarperCollinsPublishers Ltd 2003

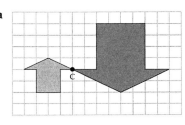
Key Words
  - congruent
  - congruency

Plenary

- Ask the class to write in their books the four conditions which show that two triangles are congruent.

Homework

1 Show that each of the following pairs of triangles are congruent. Give reasons for your answers and
   state which condition of congruency you are using.

a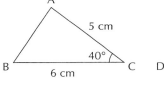

b

c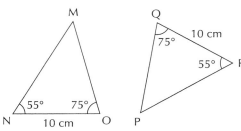

d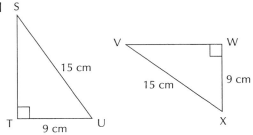

2 ABCD is a rectangle and E is the mid-point
   of AB.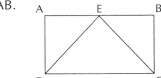

   Explain why ΔAED is congruent to ΔBEC.

Answers
1 a ∠C = ∠D, BC = DE, AC = DF (SAS)
   b GH = JK, GI = JL, HI = KL (SSS)
   c ∠N = ∠R, ∠O = ∠Q, NO = QR (ASA)
   d ∠T = ∠W = 90°, SU = VX (hypotenuse),
      TU = WX (RHS)
2 AE = EB, AD = BC, ∠A = ∠B (SAS)

Algebra 5

Framework objectives – Expand and simplify
Simplify or transform algebraic expressions by taking out single-term common factors.

Oral and mental starter

- Ask the students how many pounds equal one kilogram in weight. Accept the answer 2 as a start and work towards (or point out) the correct answer which is 2.2.
- Now ask what the equivalent of 6 kg is in pounds. Ask them how they worked this out, probably $6 \times 2 = 12$ added to $6 \times 0.2 = 1.2$ giving 13.2.
- Using a target board such as the one shown, work your way around the class asking students for pound equivalents of kilogram weights.

8	5	15	4	7
3	12	9	11	20
10	13	100	2	3

Main lesson activity

- Draw a rectangle on the board showing the **dimensions** 4 cm and 5 cm and ask the class to give you the area of the rectangle. When someone gives you the correct answer (20 cm²), ask them how they calculated it (4 cm × 5 cm).
- Draw a second rectangle on the board, this time showing the dimensions $4x$ and 3 cm. Again, ask the class for the area of the rectangle. This should provoke some discussion leading to the correct answer of $12x$. (The units are not an important issue for this lesson, so ignore them.)
- If this caused a problem, draw a further rectangle, say $5x$ by 2 cm (area of $10x$). Again, ignore the units.
- Now draw on the board a rectangle with the dimensions $3x + 2$ and 5. Again, ask the class for the area of the rectangle. The correct answer ($15x + 10$) will be seen by some students more easily than others.
- Show how this rectangle could be split up using the $3x$ and the 2 to give two rectangles – one with the dimensions $3x$ and 5 and the other with the dimensions 2 and 5. This should help all the students see that they need to find the area of each part and add them together to give the total area ($15x + 10$).
- Show that the last example is the same as $5(3x + 2)$ and link this with the finding of the area using two rectangles. Show that we expand the brackets by multiplying each term to arrive at $15x + 10$.
- Now draw on the board a rectangle with the dimensions $4x + 3$ and $2x$. Again, ask the class for the area of the rectangle. Lead the students through the splitting up of the rectangle to give two rectangles – one with the dimensions $4x$ and $2x$ and the other with the dimensions 3 and $2x$. These can then be multiplied to find the area of each rectangle and added together to give the total area $8x^2 + 6x$. Again, show the link to the **expansion** of the bracket $2x(4x + 3)$.
- Now put on the board the expression $3(4x + 2)$ and ask the class what this might mean. You are looking for the response 'the area of a rectangle with dimensions 3 and $4x + 2$' as well as the expansion of the brackets to give $12x + 6$.
- Repeat the process for $x(3x + 2)$ to give $3x^2 + 2x$.
- Put on the board the expression $3(4x – 1)$ and ask the class what this might represent. One answer is a rectangle with sides $4x – 1$ and 3. Show how, if this is split into two rectangles, what we have is a larger box with the dimensions $4x$ by 3 with a smaller box with the dimensions 1 and 3 taken off of it.
- Show that the expansion of $3(4x – 1)$ can be done in the same way as before to give $12x – 3$.

- **The class can now do Exercise 11A from Pupil Book 2.**

1 a $3x + 6$ **b** $5t + 20$ **c** $4m + 12$ **d** $2y + 14$ **e** $12 + 4m$ **f** $6 + 3k$ **g** $5 + 5t$ **h** $14 + 7x$
2 a $2x - 6$ **b** $4t - 12$ **c** $3m - 12$ **d** $6y - 30$ **e** $20 - 5m$ **f** $6 - 2k$ **g** $8 - 4t$ **h** $15 - 3x$
3 a $8x + 8$ **b** $18t - 24$ **c** $10m - 15$ **d** $9y + 21$ **e** $9 - 9m$ **f** $8 + 16k$ **g** $6 - 12t$ **h** $4 + 6x$
4 a $12t + 3$ **b** $15x + 10$ **c** $10x - 2$ **d** $24x - 8$ **e** $28t - 14$
5 a $x^2 + 3x$ **b** $t^2 + 5t$ **c** $m^2 + 4m$ **d** $y^2 + 8y$ **e** $2m + m^2$ **f** $3k + k^2$ **g** $2t + t^2$ **h** $5x + x^2$
6 a $x^2 - 2x$ **b** $t^2 - 4t$ **c** $m^2 - 3m$ **d** $y^2 - 6y$ **e** $5m - m^2$ **f** $2k - k^2$ **g** $3t - t^2$ **h** $6x - x^2$
7 a $4x^2 + 3x$ **b** $2t^2 - 3t$ **c** $3m^2 - 2m$ **d** $4y^2 + 5y$ **e** $4m - 5m^2$ **f** $3k + 2k^2$ **g** $4t - 3t^2$ **h** $x + 4x^2$
8 a $2x^2 + 3x$ **b** $5t - 3t^2$ **c** $4m + 5m^2$ **d** $7k^2 - 2k$
9 a $9x + 14$ **b** $10t + 27$ **c** $18 - 8m$ **d** $2k + 26$ **e** $4x - 12$ **f** $9x - 7$ **g** $6 - x$ **h** $8 - 2x$ **i** $13m + 2$ **j** $16m - 3$
   k $4x - 7$ **l** $6x - 36$ **m** $9x - 14$ **n** $14x - 19$
10 a $AB = y - 5$ **b** $AB = 3y$ **c** $AB = y + 1$ **d** $AB = 4y + 1$
     $CD = 4x - 1$ $CD = x + 3$ $CD = 3x - 3$ $CD = 3x + 1$

---

1 One possible method for each is shown.
 a $\frac{1}{a} + \frac{1}{b} = \frac{b}{ab} + \frac{a}{ab} = \frac{(b + a)}{ab} = \frac{(a + b)}{ab}$
 b $\frac{a}{b} + \frac{c}{d} = \frac{ad}{bd} + \frac{bc}{bd} = \frac{(ad + bc)}{bd}$
2 b It is always the same number you started with.
 c x [multiply by 3] $= 3x$ [add 15] $= 3x + 15 \rightarrow$ [divide by 3] $= x + 5$ [subtract 5] $= x$

Plenary

Key Words

- Put on the board a rectangle with dimensions $3x + 7$ and $4x$. Ask the class for the area of the rectangle.
- Now put on the board a rectangle with the dimensions $x + 7$ and $x + 3$. Again, ask the class for the area of the rectangle.
- This should provoke discussion whereby the rectangle with dimensions $x + 7$ and $x + 3$ is split into four rectangles with a total area of $x^2 + 7x + 3x + 21$.

☐ **dimension**
☐ **expansion**

Homework

1 Expand each of the following.

 a $5(3x + 1)$ **b** $7(4t - 3)$ **c** $6(3m - 2)$ **d** $4(2y + 8)$

 e $2(5 - 4m)$ **f** $3(3 + 2k)$ **g** $5(2 - 3t)$ **h** $3(4 + 2x)$

2 Expand each of the following.

 a $x(x + 4)$ **b** $t(t + 3)$ **c** $m(m + 8)$ **d** $y(y + 5)$

 e $m(3 + m)$ **f** $k(5 + k)$ **g** $t(1 + t)$ **h** $x(9 + x)$

 i $x(3x + 4)$ **j** $t(3t - 1)$ **k** $m(4m - 3)$ **l** $y(5y + 3)$

 m $m(5 - 4m)$ **n** $k(1 + 6k)$ **o** $t(3 - 4t)$ **p** $x(2 + 5x)$

3 Expand and simplify each of the following.

 a $4(x + 1) + 3(2 + 3x)$ **b** $5(t + 2) + 2(4 + 2t)$

 c $3(m + 2) + 2(1 - 3m)$ **d** $4(2k + 3) + 2(1 - 3k)$

 e $5(3x - 2) + 3(2 - 4x)$ **f** $4(5x + 2) + 5(1 - 5x)$

Answers
 1 a $15x + 5$ **b** $28t - 21$ **c** $18m - 12$ **d** $8y + 32$ **e** $10 - 8m$ **f** $9 + 6k$ **g** $10 - 15t$ **h** $12 + 6x$
 2 a $x^2 + 4x$ **b** $t^2 + 3t$ **c** $m^2 + 8m$ **d** $y^2 + 5y$ **e** $3m + m^2$ **f** $5k + k^2$ **g** $t + t^2$ **h** $9x + x^2$ **i** $3x^2 + 4x$
  j $3t^2 - t$ **k** $4m^2 - 3m$ **l** $5y^2 + 3y$ **m** $5m - 4m^2$ **n** $k + 6k^2$ **o** $3t - 4t^2$ **p** $2x + 5x^2$
 3 a $13x + 10$ **b** $9t + 18$ **c** $8 - 3m$ **d** $2k + 14$ **e** $3x - 4$ **f** $13 - 5x$

Framework objectives – Factorising

Simplify or transform algebraic expressions by taking out single-term common factors.

Oral and mental starter

- A formula for the approximate conversion of temperatures from degrees Fahrenheit to degrees Celsius is $C = \frac{1}{2}(F - 32)$, where C is the temperature in degrees Celsius and F is the temperature in degrees Fahrenheit.
- Ask the class to use this formula to estimate the equivalent of 100 °Fahrenheit in °Celsius (Answer 34). Discuss with the class the strategy they used to do this mentally.
- Work through a couple more examples, such as:

$$66 \boxed{-30} \longrightarrow 36 \boxed{-2} \longrightarrow 34 \boxed{\div 2} \longrightarrow 17$$

$$90 \boxed{-30} \longrightarrow 60 \boxed{-2} \longrightarrow 58 \boxed{\div 2} \longrightarrow 29$$

- Using a target board such as the one shown, work your way around the class asking the students to convert temperatures in °Fahrenheit to their approximate equivalents in °Celsius.

34	109	38	40	73
55	42	76	89	50
61	32	57	71	88
99	93	103	67	72

Main lesson activity

- Put on the board a rectangle with 7 cm² written inside. Ask the class what dimensions the rectangle could have. The simplest answer is 1 cm by 7 cm. Explain that coming up with these numbers involves finding a pair of factors.
- Now put on the board a rectangle with the area 12 cm² written inside. Again, ask the class what dimensions the rectangle could have. There is more than one simple choice here, and any factor pair will do (e.g. 2 cm by 6 cm, 3 cm by 4 cm).
- Now put on the board a rectangle with the expression $3x + 3$ written inside. Tell the class that this is the area of the rectangle and ask what dimensions the rectangle could have. Lead the discussion so the class reaches the correct answer of 3 and $x + 1$.
- In order to reach the answer above, we have to find a pair of factors which when multiplied together give $3x + 3$. Explain that this is called **factorising** and is the opposite process of expansion which they covered in the previous lesson.
- Put on the board the expression $6x + 9$ and tell them to imagine that this is the area of a rectangle. Ask them what the dimensions of the rectangle could be. They need to factorise the expression to create a bracket with a term outside – the two factors. For this example, factorisation gives $3(2x + 3)$. Show that this expands to give $6x + 9$.
- Now put on the board the expression $x^2 + 5x$ and again ask what dimensions a rectangle of this area could have. Help the class to see that this factorisation will be $x(x + 5)$, again showing that the expansion will give the original expression.

- **The class can now do Exercise 11B from Pupil Book 2.**

112   © HarperCollins*Publishers* Ltd 2003

1 **a** $3(x + 2)$ **b** $2(2t + 3)$ **c** $4(m + 2)$ **d** $5(y + 2)$ **e** $2(4 + m)$ **f** $3(1 + 2k)$
   g $5(1 + 3t)$ **h** $3(4 + x)$
2 **a** $2(x - 2)$ **b** $4(t - 3)$ **c** $3(m - 3)$ **d** $3(2y - 3)$ **e** $7(2 - m)$ **f** $3(7 - k)$
   g $4(3 - 2t)$ **h** $3(5 - x)$
3 **a** $3(4x + 1)$ **b** $2(3t - 2)$ **c** $3(3m - 1)$ **d** $3(y + 2)$ **e** $3(5 - m)$ **f** $4(3 + k)$
   g $2(3 - t)$ **h** $3(9 + x)$
4 **a** $3x + 4$ **b** $5 + 3t$ **c** $2m - 3$ **d** $4 - 2t$
5 **a** $x(x + 3)$ **b** $t(t + 4)$ **c** $m(m + 5)$ **d** $y(y + 7)$ **e** $m(3 + m)$ **f** $k(4 + k)$
   g $t(3 + t)$ **h** $x(1 + x)$
6 **a** $x(x - 3)$ **b** $t(3t - 5)$ **c** $m(m - 2)$ **d** $y(4y - 5)$ **e** $m(2 - m)$ **f** $k(4 - 3k)$
   g $t(5 - t)$ **h** $x(7 - 4x)$
7 **a** $x(3x + 4)$ **b** $t(5t - 3)$ **c** $m(3m - 2)$ **d** $y(4y + 5)$ **e** $m(4 - 3m)$ **f** $k(2 + 5k)$
   g $t(4 - 3t)$ **h** $x(2 + 7x)$
8 **a** $3x + 4$ **b** $2 + 3m$ **c** $3 - 2t$ **d** $4x - 1$
9 **a** $n, n + 1, n + 2$ **b** $3n + 3$ **c** $3(n + 1)$
   d $(n + 1)$ is an integer, say m, hence $3(n + 1) = 3m$, a multiple of 3

a $(2$ and $x^2 + 2x)$, $(x$ and $2x + 4)$, $(2x$ and $x + 2)$
b For $x = 1$, all pairs of values multiply to give an area of 6; for $x = 2$, all pairs of values multiply to give an area of 16; for $x = 3$, all pairs of values multiply to give an area of 30.
c $(2$ and $6x^2 + 9x)$, $(3$ and $4x^2 + 6x)$, $(6$ and $2x^2 + 3x)$, $(x$ and $12x + 18)$, $(2x$ and $6x + 9)$, $(3x$ and $4x + 6)$, $(6x$ and $2x + 3)$

Plenary

- Ask the class what is meant by factorisation. You want responses that show understanding of a breaking down of an expression into two terms that will multiply together to give the original.
- Show them again the two stages they have gone through today with some examples such as:
   $6 + 9x = 3(2 + 3x)$
   $5x^2 - 3x = x(5x - 3)$

Key Words

☐ **factorisation**

Homework

1 Factorise each of the following.

a $3x + 9$	**b** $4t + 12$	**c** $2m + 8$	**d** $5y + 15$
e $10 + 2m$	**f** $4 + 6k$	**g** $10 + 15t$	**h** $12 + 9x$
i $6x - 4$	**j** $8t - 12$	**k** $6m - 9$	**l** $20y - 8$
m $21 - 7m$	**n** $18 - 3k$	**o** $12 - 10t$	**p** $15 - 5x$

2 Factorise each of the following.

a $x^2 + 5x$	**b** $t^2 + 3t$	**c** $m^2 + 4m$	**d** $y^2 + 8y$
e $6m + m^2$	**f** $2k + k^2$	**g** $7t + t^2$	**h** $x + x^2$
i $x^2 - 4x$	**j** $2t^2 - 3t$	**k** $m^2 - 5m$	**l** $5y^2 - 4y$
m $3m - m^2$	**n** $6k - 5k^2$	**o** $6t - t^2$	**p** $8x - 5x^2$

Answers
1 **a** $3(x + 3)$ **b** $4(t + 3)$ **c** $2(m + 4)$ **d** $5(y + 3)$ **e** $2(5 + m)$ **f** $2(2 + 3k)$ **g** $5(2 + 3t)$ **h** $3(4 + 3x)$
   i $2(3x - 2)$ **j** $4(2t - 3)$ **k** $3(2m - 3)$ **l** $4(5y - 2)$ **m** $7(3 - m)$ **n** $3(6 - k)$ **o** $2(6 - 5t)$ **p** $5(3 - x)$
2 **a** $x(x + 5)$ **b** $t(t + 3)$ **c** $m(m + 4)$ **d** $y(y + 8)$ **e** $m(6 + m)$ **f** $k(2 + k)$ **g** $t(7 + t)$ **h** $x(1 + x)$
   i $x(x - 4)$ **j** $t(2t - 3)$ **k** $m(m - 5)$ **l** $y(5y - 4)$ **m** $m(3 - m)$ **n** $k(6 - 5k)$ **o** $t(6 - t)$ **p** $x(8 - 5x)$

Framework objectives – Substitution

Substitute numbers into expressions and formulae.

Use formulae from mathematics and other subjects.

Oral and mental starter

- This starter is concerned with calculating percentages.
- Set percentages in context by talking about getting a 20% reduction for a certain item you purchased recently.
- Ask the class how they would calculate 20% of a value. They might use the strategy of finding the value of 10% and then doubling it or they might divide the full value by 5.
- Give students an example, such as 'What is 20% of £34'. Work though the example using the first method which most students will find more straightforward, i.e. 10% of £34 is £3.40, doubling it gives 20% as £6.80.
- Using a target board such as the one shown, work your way around the class asking students to work out 20% of the given value.

£45	35 kg	50 minutes	£82	29 kg
45 minutes	£67	18 m	2 hours	£29
130 kg	180 minutes	£89	75 kg	49 m
£234	83 m	24 hours	£26	130 kg

Main lesson activity

- This lesson is about **substitution**. You could introduce the topic by talking about the importance of substitution in football or through some other context which is more suitable for your students. The main point to get across is how important and useful substitution can be.
- Similarly, in mathematics substitution is an essential tool.
- Put on the board the expression $3x^2$. Ask the students what this value will be when $x = 5$. The answer is 75. Make sure that the students remember that they need to square the 5 before multiplying by 3.
- Now ask them to substitute $x = -5$. What difference will this make? Because squaring -5 gives the same result as squaring 5, the answer is the same.
- Now ask the class to substitute a more awkward number, for example 0.2 Again, they must square first to give 0.04, then multiply by 3 to give 0.12 You might need to give the students some practise multiplying decimal values.
- Now put on the board $3x^2 + 5$ and ask the class to substitute $x = -2$. Square -2 to give 4, multiply by 3 to give 12 then add on the 5 to give 17.
- Put on the board the formula $C = \frac{1}{2}(F - 32)$. Remind the class that this is the formula for the approximate conversion from degrees Fahrenheit to degrees Celsius. Explain to the class that in order to use this formula to find the equivalent temperature of 100 °F in degrees Celsius, we need to substitute $F = 100$ into the formula: $C = \frac{1}{2}(100 - 32) = \frac{1}{2} \times 68 = 34$.
- **The class can now do Exercise 3C from Pupil Book 2.**

1 a i 16 ii 9 iii 0.01 b i 25 ii 16 iii 0.04 c i 12 ii 3 iii 0.75
 d i 36 ii 16 iii 4.84 e i 23 ii 16 iii 7.09 f i 28 ii 19 iii 3.01
 g i 14 ii 30 iii 7.25 h i 50 ii 10 iii 1.16 i i 16 ii 7 iii 4.03
 j i 67 ii 103 iii 4
2 a i 8 ii –1000 iii 0.008 b i 16 ii –2000 iii 0.054 c i 24 ii –3000
 iii 0.046875 d i 12 ii –1500 iii 5.0625 e i 6 ii –750
 iii 39.55 (rounded)
3 a 32 °F b 93.56 °F c 17.6 °F
4 £258.75 = £259 to nearest pound

Extension Answers

 a 84 b 459

Plenary

Key Words

☐ **substitution**

- Talk to the class about substitution being one of the major aspects of algebra that is used by lots of people. Every day, millions of people are substituting into formulae to calculate something, for example bank cashiers when converting foreign currencies.
- Many computer programmes rely heavily on substitution of data that come in from many different sources.

Homework

1 a Find the value of x^2 when i $x = 5$ ii $x = -2$ iii $x = 0.2$
 b Find the value of $3x^2$ when i $x = 6$ ii $x = -3$ iii $x = 0.4$
 c Find the value of $3x^2 + 2$ when i $x = 3$ ii $x = -1$ iii $x = 0.6$
 d Find the value of $4x^2 - 3$ when i $x = 5$ ii $x = -2$ iii $x = 1.5$
 e Find the value of $\dfrac{x^2 + 7}{5}$ when i $x = 8$ ii $x = -6$ iii $x = 2.3$

2 a Find the value of p^3 when i $p = 4$ ii $p = -20$ iii $p = 0.5$
 b Find the value of $4p^3 + 2$ when i $p = 3$ ii $p = -10$ iii $p = 0.1$
 c Find the value of $5p^3 - 4$ when i $p = 2$ ii $p = -10$ iii $p = 0.75$
 d Find the value of $\dfrac{2p^3}{5}$ when i $p = 1$ ii $p = -1$ iii $p = 2.5$

Answers
 1 a i 25 ii 4 iii 0.04 b i 108 ii 27 iii 0.48 c i 29 ii 5 iii 3.08 d i 97 ii 13 iii 6
 e i 14.2 ii 8.6 iii 2.458
 2 a i 64 ii –8000 iii 0.125 b i 110 ii –3998 iii 2.004 c i 36 ii –5004 iii –1.890625
 d i 0.4 ii –0.4 iii 6.25

Framework objectives – Change of subject
Derive a formula and, in simple cases, change its subject.

Oral and mental starter

- Ask the class who sends text messages to their friends. Ask several of the students who do, how much they cost.
- Put on the board the different rates for text messages. At the time of printing, these are generally 8p, 10p or 12p, but do use those that your students offer, unless they only offer 10p!
- Ask how many text messages the students send per day. Using the price per message that the student quoted earlier, work out how much various students spend on text messaging per day.
- Ask other students how many messages they send per week. Again, using the price per message, work out how much various students spend on text messaging per week.
- Talk about top up cards costing £10, £15 or £20. How many text messages can the students send from one top up at the different values?
- This is a rich source of mental work that works best when the real live data is being used, i.e. current charges. Try not to be exclusive. If there are some students not able to text, ensure that the wording is such that they are included in the discussions.
- This can be expanded into estimating how many text messages each student might make in a year and therefore how much this will cost.

Main lesson activity

- This lesson is about changing the subject of a formula. You could introduce the topic of changing by asking the students how often they get changed.
- Bring the class round to formulae and the fact that as well as us, formulae also need to change depending on what they need to do.
- Put on the board the formula $C = 250 + 5W$. Explain that this formula is used to calculate the cost for advertisements in a certain newspaper, where C is the cost in pence of the advertisement and W is the number of words in the advertisement. Explain that C is the **subject of the formula** because it is the variable (letter) in the formula which stands on its own, usually on the left-hand side of the equals sign.
- Ask how much it would cost to place an advertisement with 20 words in the newspaper. Use this example to verify that all the students can substitute $W = 20$ into the formula to get $C = 250 + 5 \times 20 = 250 + 100 = 350$, giving the cost as £3.50.
- Now tell the class that you want to place an advertisement in the newspaper and that you have £10 to pay for the advertisement. Ask them how many words you can use in the advertisement.
- In order to work this out, they need to rearrange the formula so W is the subject.
- Remind the class that the same rules apply that they have used previously with formulae, that is that we change both sides at the same time by doing the same thing to both sides, keeping the balance of the formula.
- Work through the example. We need to get W on its own, so start by simplifying the right-hand side of the formula:

$$C = 250 + 5W$$

subtracting 250 from both sides gives: $\quad C - 250 = 5W$

dividing both sides by 5 gives: $\quad \dfrac{C - 250}{5} = W$

turning the expression round gives: $\quad W = \dfrac{C - 250}{5}$

- **The class can now do Exercise 11D from Pupil Book 2.**

1 a i $I = \dfrac{V}{R}$ **ii** $R = \dfrac{V}{I}$ **b i** $U = S - FT$ **ii** $F = \dfrac{(S - U)}{T}$ **iii** $T = \dfrac{(S - U)}{F}$

  c i $b = \dfrac{(P - 2w)}{2}$ **ii** $w = \dfrac{(P - 2b)}{2}$ **d i** $b = \dfrac{2A}{h}$ **ii** $h = \dfrac{2A}{b}$

2 a $C = \dfrac{5(F - 32)}{9}$ **b i** −53.9 °C **ii** 19.2 °C **iii** 13.6 °C

3 a 24.5 cm² **b** 11.8 cm²

4 a £1.60 **b** 0.75 cm

5 a 125.7 cm² **b** 9.6 cm (9.5 cm if π key on calculator used) **c** 1.5 cm

6 a $N = 5$, $R = 3$, $A = 6$, so $N + R - A = 5 + 3 - 6 = 2$, so $N + R - A = 2$.

  c $N + R - A = 2$, so $N + R = 2 + A$, so $N + R - 2 = A$,

    i.e. $A = N + R - 2$. $N = 10$, $R = 9$, so $A = 17$

1 a $r = \sqrt{(A/\pi)}$ **b** $r = \sqrt{(V/\pi h)}$ **c** $r = \sqrt[3]{(3V/4\pi)}$ **2** 5.64 cm **3** 2.66 cm

Plenary

Key Words

- Discuss with the class the similarities between the processes of changing the subject of a formula and solving equations.
- To close the lesson, you might like to work with the class to make T the subject of the following formula:

$$W = \dfrac{3K + 5T^2}{4}$$

□ **subject of a formula**

Homework

1 Change the subject of each of the following formulae as indicated.

  a Make I the subject of the formula $W = IPT$.

  b i Make P the subject of $F = P + MK$.

    ii Make M the subject of $F = P + MK$.

  c i Make m the subject of $T = 3m + 2n$.

    ii Make n the subject of $T = 3m + 2n$.

  d Make b the subject of $V = \dfrac{abh}{3}$.

2 The formula $C = \dfrac{19R}{8} + 40$ is used to calculate the cost in pounds of making a boiler of radius R (cm).

  a Make R the subject of the formula.

  b Use this formula to find the radius of a boiler that cost £150 to make.

Answers

  1 a $I = \dfrac{W}{PT}$ **b i** $P = F - MK$ **ii** $M = \dfrac{(F - P)}{K}$ **c i** $m = \dfrac{(T - 2n)}{3}$ **ii** $n = \dfrac{(T - 3m)}{2}$

    d $b = \dfrac{3V}{ah}$

  2 a $R = \dfrac{8(C - 40)}{19}$ **b** 46.3 cm

Framework objectives – Graphs of linear functions

Generate points and plot graphs of linear functions (y given implicitly in terms of x), e.g. $ay + bx = 0$, $y + bx + c = 0$, on paper and using ICT.

Oral and mental starter

- Ask the students to put their hands up if they can multiply by 11. Many hands will go up.
- Tell them to keep their hands up if they can work out 11×28 in their heads. Discuss the different strategies the students have used to get their various answers.
- One strategy is to do it in two parts and add them together: $11 \times 28 = (10 \times 28) + (1 \times 28) = 280 + 28 = 308$.
- Go through another example using this method with them: $11 \times 34 = (10 \times 34) + (1 \times 34) = 340 + 34 = 374$.
- Using a target board such as the one shown, work your way around the class asking students to multiply the given number by 11.

17	25	51	67	92
42	78	19	34	83
94	85	36	48	23

Main lesson activity

- Put on the board a pair of axes labelled from –4 to 10 on both axes.
- Then write the equation $y - 4x + 3 = 0$ on the board. Ask the class if they can tell you anything about the graph of this equation. Establish that it's a linear equation so the graph will be a straight line.
- Ask for some ideas from the class as to how we could find out what the graph should be like? Lead them through the stages of:
  i rearranging the formula
  ii creating a table of values to give some coordinates
  iii plotting the coordinates to enable us to draw a graph.
- Go through each of the above stages for the above example $y - 4x + 3 = 0$
  i Rearrange the formula to make y the subject: $y = 4x - 3$
  ii Create a table using suggested sensible values:
  iii Plot those point which fall within the axes you drew at the beginning of the lesson. This gives a straight line.

x	–1	0	1	2	3
y	–7	–3	1	5	9

- Repeat the above with further examples if necessary to ensure that all the students follow each stage as this is essential to the exercise.

- **The class can now do Exercise 11E from Pupil Book 2.**

Plenary

Key Words

☐ **linear**

● Confirm with the class that they are now able to plot a graph from any linear
  equation they are given. Ask them what stages they need to go through in order
  to be able to draw the graph:
   i ensure one variable is the subject of a formula
   ii complete a table of values to give coordinates
   iii plot the coordinates
   iv draw the straight line graph.

Homework

1 **i** Copy and complete the following tables of values for each of the given equations.

  ii Use each table to draw the graph of its equation.

  a $y - 2x - 3 = 0$

x	−1	0	1	2	3
y					

  b $y - 3x + 2 = 0$

x	−1	0	1	2	3
y					

2 Draw a graph of each of the following equations on the same pair of axes.

  a $y - 2x - 1 = 0$ **b** $y - 2x - 3 = 0$ **c** $y - 2x + 1 = 0$ **d** $y - 2x + 3 = 0$

  Comment on the similarities and differences between the graphs.

Answers
  1 **a i** y: 1, 3, 5, 7, 9 **b i** y: −5, −2, 1, 4, 7
  2 All the graphs should be parallel to each other ($y = 2x$) and they all cut the y axis at the negative value of the
    constant in the equation.

Solving Problems and Revision

Framework objectives – Fractions, percentages and decimals

Revision of Number:

Solve increasingly demanding problems and evaluate solutions.

Solve problems involving percentage changes.

Use proportional reasoning to solve a problem, choosing the correct numbers to take as 100%, or as a whole.

Oral and mental starter

- The following is a 10-question, SATs-style, mental test on the theme of fractions. Repeat each question twice and allow 10 seconds to answer.
  1 What is one-seventh of 28?
  2 What is the next number in this sequence where each number is one third of the previous number?
     Fifty four, eighteen, six, two, ...
  3 What fraction of one metre is thirty five centimetres? [Write '1 m' and '35 cm' on the board.]
  4 One fifth of a number is twelve. What is the number?
  5 Look at these numbers. Which one of them is the decimal equivalent of three-eighths? [Write the decimals on the board.]
        0.38   3.8   0.375   3.125   3.08
  6 What is half of 4.7?
  7 Write seven-tenths as a decimal.
  8 What is the sum of three-eighths and one-quarter?
  9 Add one point six to one quarter.
  10 What is three-quarters squared? [Write $\left(\dfrac{3}{4}\right)^2$ on the board.]

  Answers 1 4 **2** $\frac{2}{3}$ **3** $\frac{35}{100}$ or equivalent $\frac{7}{20}$ **4** 60 **5** 0.375 **6** 2.35
  7 0.7 **8** $\frac{5}{8}$ or equivalent (0.625) **9** 1.85 **10** $\frac{9}{16}$

Main lesson activity

- This is a revision lesson on Number, principally covering fractions, decimals and percentages.
  The questions in the Pupil Book exercise are graded from Level 4 to Level 7 as follows:

Q. 1, 2, 3, 4, 5	**Level 4**
Q. 6, 9, 10	**Level 5**
Q. 7, 11, 12, 13	**Level 6**
Q. 8	**Level 7**

- Before letting students start the questions you can go through key points (as suggested below) or discuss some specific questions with the class to remind them of the methods used.

General
  ○ Equivalence of fractions, percentages and decimals

Fractions
  ○ Equivalent fractions
  ○ Cancelling
  ○ Converting mixed numbers to top heavy fractions and vice versa
  ○ Adding and subtracting fractions

Decimals
- ○ Ordering
- ○ Changing between metric measurement units

Percentages
- ○ Finding a percentage of a quantity
- ○ Finding one quantity as a percentage of another
- ○ Calculating percentage increase and decrease

- ● **The class can now do Exercise 12A from Pupil Book 2.**

Exercise 12A Answers

1 a i 22% **ii** 44% **b i** 29% **ii** 58%
2 60%, 0.60, $\frac{3}{5}$ and $\frac{6}{10}$
3 $\frac{7}{12}$
4 £55.50
5 a 5.19 m **b** 22.65 km
6 a $\frac{14}{15}$ **b** $\frac{7}{18}$ **c** $4\frac{3}{20}$
7 134.4
8 a i 0.08 **ii** 2000 **b** 400–450
9 74.55 kg
10 £63.05
11 £36.21
12 a 200 000 **b** 425 000 **c** 3.9%
13 a 31.4% **b** 36% **c** Unleaded 76.2p per litre. Lead replacement 77p per litre

---

Plenary

- ● Go through the answers to the exercise. Discuss and clarify those with which students had difficulty.

Homework

It is assumed that during the revision period students will be given a past SATs paper to work through at home. Students will have seen some questions before in the *Maths Frameworking* Pupil Books, so two mock SATs papers (tier 4–6 and 5–7) are provided in this Teacher's Pack, after the Chapter 12 lesson plans. These mock papers consist of SATs-style questions which students will not have encountered before.

Additional homework questions are provided below, for further practice on the topics covered in this lesson.

Homework

1 Work out $17\frac{1}{2}$% of £84.

2 a Calculate 12% of £36.50. **b** Work out $17\frac{1}{2}$% of £113.

Answers
1 £14.70
2 a £4.38 **b** £19.78

LESSON 12.2

Framework objectives – Long multiplication and division; ratio; directed numbers

Revision of Number:

Solve increasingly demanding problems and evaluate solutions.

Interpret and use ratio in a range of contexts, including solving word problems.

Oral and mental starter

- The following is a 10-question, SATs-style, mental test on the theme of percentages. Repeat each question twice and allow 10 seconds to answer.

  1 In a group of sixty animals, thirty were rabbits. What percentage were rabbits?

  2 The pie chart shows information from a survey of the favourite foods of some teenagers. [Draw the chart shown on the board.]
  What percentage of the teenagers did not pick burgers?

  3 What percentage is the same as the fraction one-fifth?

  4 What is ten percent of thirty five pounds?

  5 What is twenty percent of two hundred pounds?

  6 A survey identified how many people in a village own dogs. The percentage bar chart shows the results of the survey. [Draw the chart shown on the board, with a ratio of 40 : 60.]
  Estimate the percentage of the people who own dogs.

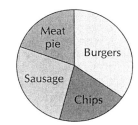

Own dogs	Don't own dogs

0%   100%

  7 Thirty percent of a number is nine. What is the number?

  8 A CD costing thirteen pounds is reduced in a sale by ten percent. What is the new price of the CD?

  9 There are 20 chocolates in a box, of which 12 have soft centres. What percentage of the chocolates have soft centres?

  10 Fifteen percent of a number is twelve. What is the number?

  Answers 1 50% **2** 60–70% **3** 20% **4** £3.50 **5** £40 **6** 35–45%
  7 30 **8** £11.70 **9** 60% **10** 80

Main lesson activity

- This is a revision lesson on Number, principally covering long multiplication and division.

- The questions in the Pupil Book exercise are graded from Level 4 to Level 7 as follows:

Q. 1, 2, 3	**Level 4**
Q. 4, 5, 10, 11	**Level 5**
Q. 6, 7, 12, 13	**Level 6**
Q. 8	**Level 7**

- Before letting students start the questions you can go through key points (as suggested below) or discuss some specific questions with the class to remind them of the methods used.

General
- ○ Basic knowledge of tables up to 10×10

Four rules
- ○ Setting out in columns for addition and subtraction
- ○ Using box method or column methods for long multiplication
- ○ Using chunking for long division

Directed numbers
○ Using a number line
○ Combining signs when adding and subtracting: ++, −+, etc

Ratio
○ Adding ratios
○ Dividing up an amount into a given ratio
○ Multiplying by a ratio to get individual amounts

● **The class can now do Exercise 12B from Pupil Book 2.**

Exercise 12B Answers

1 **a i** < **ii** > **iii** > **b i** 1 and −2, 3 and −4, or 5 and −6 **ii** −11 **iii** −8 − 5 = −13
2 **a** 63 **b** 18 **c** 170 **d** 100
3 **a** 9 + 6 = 20 − 5 **b** 15 − 3 = 4 × 3 **c** 5 − 2 = 15 ÷ 5 *or* 5 × 2 = 15 − 5
 d 8 ÷ 4 = 4 ÷ 2 *or* 8 ÷ 4 = 4 − 2
4 £31.36
5 17 bins with £7 left over
6 £18
7 **a** 14.4 **b** 90 **c** 0.06
8 **a** 5^9 **b** -2^6 and 8^2 **c** 4^4 **d** $(-1)^2$, $(-2)^6$, 8^2 and 5^9
9 **a** 508.4 **b** 2.5 **c** 12.5 **d** 10.4
10 **a** 15 **b** £56 175 **c** £80.25
11 **a** 52 mph **b** 4 hours and 40 minutes
12 **a** 400 kg **b** 8 bags
13 347 tickets

Plenary

● Go through the answers to the exercise. Discuss and clarify those with which
students had difficulty.

Homework

1 **a** For an expedition to the Himalayas, 185 bottles of oxygen costing £47 each are
 ordered.

 How much will the oxygen cost in total?

 b The expedition takes 2080 ready-meals. These are to be packed into boxes with 16 meals in
 each.

 How many boxes will be needed?

2 The label on a jar of Yeast Extract says that each 100 g contains 1500% of the recommended daily
 intake of Vitamin B12.

 How many grams of the yeast extract will be needed to give exactly the recommended daily intake
 of Vitamin B12?

Answers
 1 **a** £8695 **b** 130 boxes
 2 6.67 grams

Framework objectives – Rules of algebra and linear equations
Revision of Algebra:
Represent problems and synthesise information in algebraic form.

Oral and mental starter

- The following is a 20-question, SATs-style, mental test on the theme of the four rules. Repeat each question twice and allow 10 seconds to answer.
  1. Add these numbers. [Write 78 and 74 on the board.]
  2. What number do you have to add to 123 to make two hundred?
  3. Multiply eight by seven.
  4. What number multiplied by nine makes one hundred and eight?
  5. Write the number thirty four thousand and seventy nine in figures.
  6. Write down the number that is three less than minus six.
  7. Four boxes of pencils cost six pounds. How much will seven boxes of pencils cost?
  8. Multiply nought point seven by ten.
  9. A chocolate bar costs one pound forty pence. I buy four bars. How much change will I get from a ten pound note?
  10. I am thinking of two numbers. When I add them together I get nine. When I multiply them together I get twenty. What are the numbers ?
  11. Multiply nought point six by nought point five.
  12. Double sixty six.
  13. What is the total cost of five video tapes at four pounds ninety five pence each?
  14. How many seconds are there in fifteen minutes?
  15. Work out the value of this. [Write $2^3 \times 3^2$ on the board.]
  16. What is three minus nought point two?
  17. How much must be added to this number to make one hundred. [Write 63.5 on the board.]
  18. Multiply together the first three prime numbers.
  19. I have saved thirty seven pounds in twenty pence coins. How many coins is that?
  20. Divide thirty by nought point three.
      Answers **1** 152 **2** 77 **3** 56 **4** 12 **5** 34 079 **6** –9 **7** £10.50
      8 7 **9** £4.40 **10** 4 and 5 **11** 0.3 **12** 132 **13** £24.75
      14 900 **15** 72 **16** 2.8 **17** 36.5 **18** 30 **19** 185 **20** 100

Main lesson activity

- This is a revision lesson on Algebra, principally covering the basic rules and solving linear equations.
- The questions in the Pupil Book exercise are graded from Level 4 to Level 7 as follows:

Q. 1, 2, 3	**Level 4**
Q. 4, 5, 6	**Level 5**
Q. 7, 8, 9, 10	**Level 6**
Q. 11	**Level 7**

- Before letting students start the questions you can go through key points (as suggested below) or discuss some specific questions with the class to remind them of the methods used.

Basic algebra
  ○ Using letters to represent variables
  ○ The difference between a term, an expression and an equation

Manipulative algebra
  ○ Substituting numbers into expressions
  ○ Expanding brackets
  ○ Factorising
  ○ Collecting like terms

Linear equations
- ○ Rearranging – collecting together variables and numbers on the LHS and RHS respectively
- ○ Inverse operations (change sides, change signs)
- ○ Checking answers by substituting into original equation

● **The class can now do Exercise 12C from Pupil Book 2.**

Exercise 12C Answers

1 **a** (10, 9)   **b** first value is not even

2 **a** $a = 30$, S3; $b = 2a$, S1; $b + c = 75$, S4; $\dfrac{(a + b + c)}{3}$, S2   **b** $b = 60$, $c = 15$

3 **a** $0.5n$, $n \div 2$ **b** $n^3 \div n$, $n \times n$
   c any equivalent expression different to those given, e.g. $5n - 3n$

4 **a** n^2, $4n$, 16 **b** $n^2 + 8n + 16$

5 **a** $4x - 20$ **b** $11x + 3$ **c** $5x + 2$ **d** $17x + 16$ **e** $5x + 22$

6 **a i** 21   **ii** 10   **iii** 50   **b i** $z = 3$ **ii** $z = 22$ **iii** $z = -1$

7 **a** $6x + 3 = 12$, $x = 1.5$ **b** $3y - 6 = y + 7$, $y = 6.5$

8 **a** $2n + 4$ **b** $n + 6$ **c** $-n + 2$ **d** $3n - 1$

9 **a i** 45   **ii** 26   **iii** -11 **b i** $3(x + 2y)$ **ii** $x(x + 1)$ **iii** $2a(2b + 3)$

10 **a** $x = 1.5$ **b** $x = 2$ **c** $x = -0.5$

11 **a** $3(4x - 6)$ and $6(2x - 3)$ **b** $6(y - 2)$ **c** $3y(3y - 2)$

Plenary

● Go through the answers to the exercise. Discuss and clarify those with which students had difficulty.

Homework

1 Expand the brackets in the following expressions and then simplify if possible.

   a $3(x - 4)$ **b** $2(x - 1) + 3x$ **c** $4(x + 1) + 2(x - 2)$

   d $3(2x - 4) + 4(x + 7)$ **e** $4(3x - 1) - 2(x - 5)$

2 **a** When $x = 3$ and $y = 4$ work out the value of the three expressions below.

   i $2x + 9$ **ii** $3x - 2y$ **iii** $3(5x - 3y + 4)$

   b Solve the equations below to find the value of z.

   i $2z - 9 = 21$ **ii** $z + 6 = 5$ **iii** $6z + 7 = 3z + 19$

Answers
1 **a** $3x - 12$ **b** $5x - 2$ **c** $6x$ **d** $10x + 16$ **e** $10x + 6$
2 **a i** 15   **ii** 1   **iii** 21   **b i** $z = 15$ **ii** $z = -1$ **iii** $z = 4$

Framework objectives – Graphs

Revision of Algebra:

Represent problems and synthesise information in graphical form.

Oral and mental starter

- The following is a 10-question, SATs-style, mental test on reading diagrams.
  Each student will need a sheet with the diagrams below to refer to. Teachers may
  find the Teacher's Pack CD useful to prepare these.
- Repeat each question twice and allow 10 seconds to answer.
  1 What number is the arrow pointing to?
  2 The pie chart shows the number of boys and girls in a youth club. There are
    15 girls. How many boys are there?
  3 Estimate the length of the line in centimetres.
  4 The bar chart shows the number of children in some families. How many
    families are represented?
  5 This is a centimetre grid. What is the area of the shaded square?
  6 Which diagram shows strong positive correlation?
  7 By looking at the timetable, work out how long the journey from Barnsley to
    High Green takes.
  8 What number is the arrow pointing to?
  9 Add one more square to the grid so that it has rotational symmetry of order 2.
  10 Which diagram shows the graph $x + y = 5$?

Answers   **1** 320   **2** 45   **3** 5 cm   **4** 21   **5** 17 cm^2 **6** c   **7** 44 minutes   **8** –1.4   **9**
       10 c

1

2

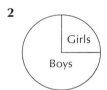

5

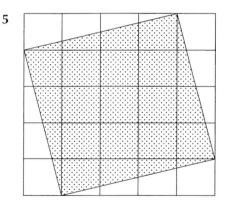

3

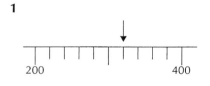

4

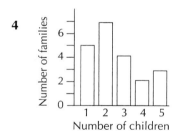

6

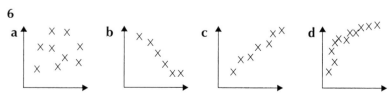

7

Barnsley	09 32
Birdwell	09 55
High Green	10 16
Sheffield	10 36

8

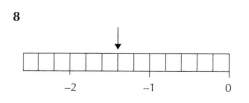

9

10

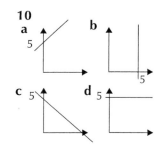

Main lesson activity

- This is a revision lesson on Algebra, principally covering graphs.
- The questions in the Pupil Book exercise are graded from Level 4 to Level 7 as follows:

Q. 1, 2, 3	**Level 4**
Q. 4, 5, 6	**Level 5**
Q. 7, 8, 9, 10	**Level 6**
Q. 11	**Level 7**

- Before letting students start the questions you can go through key points (as suggested below) or discuss some specific questions with the class to remind them of the methods used.

Basic graphs
- ○ $y = mx + c$ as the formula of a straight line
- ○ Significance of m and c for gradients, parallel lines and intercept with y–axis

Real life graphs
- ○ Travel graphs or distance–time graphs
- ○ Gradient of line represents speed
- ○ Horizontal line represents no motion

- **The class can now do Exercise 12D from Pupil Book 2.**

Exercise 12D Answers

1 a l_3 **b** l_4 **c** l_2 **d** l_1
2 See graph below
3 Yes because $2 \times 20 - 10 = 30$
4 a 10 minutes **b** 3.5 miles
5 a 7:15 **b** 7:45 **c** 8:40 **d** 9:30
6 a i no **ii** yes **iii** no **iv** yes
  b See graph below

7 a true **b** cannot be sure, graph is levelling off
  c cannot be sure – there may not be a causal link
8 a b See graph below **c** (3, 5)
9 a $y = -2$ **b** $y = -2x$ **c** $x = -0.5$ and $y = 1$
10 a See graph below **b** 13.5 square units
11 a A and E **b** C and D **c** A and F **d** D and F

Graphs

2

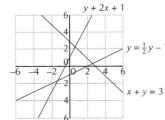

6 b

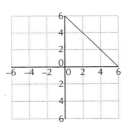

8 a b

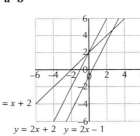

10 a

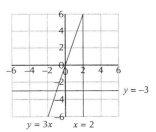

Plenary

- Go through the answers to the exercise. Discuss and clarify those with which students had difficulty.

Homework

1 Draw and label the following graphs.

  a $y = 3x + 1$ **b** $y = 3x - 1$ **c** $y = 2x + 1$

2 By drawing the graphs $y = 2x$, $y = -2$ and $x = 3$, work out the area of the triangle enclosed by all three lines.

Answers
  1 Check graphs are correct.
  2 16 square units

LESSON 12.5

Framework objectives – Shape, Space and Measures

Revision of Shape, Space and Measures:

Represent problems and synthesise information in geometric form.

Solve problems using properties of angles, of parallel and intersecting lines, and of triangles and other polygons, justifying inferences and explaining reasoning with diagrams and text.

Oral and mental starter

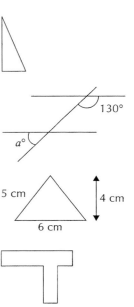

- The following is a 10-question, SATs-style, mental test on the theme of shape, space and measures. Repeat each question twice and allow 10 seconds to answer.

 1 How many lines of symmetry does a parallelogram have?

 2 A shape is folded in half along its only line of symmetry. After folding it looks like this [draw shape shown on board].
 What is the name of the original shape?

 3 I face south-east and turn anticlockwise through 270 degrees. What direction am I now facing?

 4 I drive six and a half kilometres in 10 minutes. What is my average speed in kilometres per hour?

 5 What is the value of angle a? [Draw the diagram shown on the board.]

 6 What is the area of this triangle? [Draw the triangle shown on the board.]

 7 Draw the shape that you get after rotating this T shape by 90° clockwise. [Draw the shape shown on the board.]

 8 What is the length of a rectangle with an area of 56 cm² and a width of 4 cm?

 9 What is the approximate area of a circle with a radius of 2 centimetres?

 10 The distance from home to school is about 12 kilometres. Approximately how many miles is that?

 Answers   **1** 0   **2** isosceles triangle   **3** south-west   **4** 39 km/h   **5** 50°
 6 12 cm²   **7** 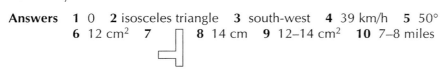   **8** 14 cm   **9** 12–14 cm²   **10** 7–8 miles

Main lesson activity

- This is a revision lesson on Shape, Space and Measures.
- The questions in the Pupil Book exercise are graded from Level 4 to Level 7 as follows:

Q. 1, 2, 3, 4, 6 a,b	**Level 4**
Q. 5 & 7	**Level 5**
Q. 6 c, 8, 9, 10, 11	**Level 6**
Q. 12	**Level 7**

- Before letting students start the questions you can go through key points (as suggested below) or discuss some specific questions with the class to remind them of the methods used.

Volume and area
 ○ Recall of formulae for area of rectangle, triangle, parallelogram, circle
 ○ Recall of formulae for volume of cubes, cuboids and prisms

Symmetry
 ○ Line symmetry
 ○ Rotational symmetry

Angles
 ○ Definition of acute, obtuse and reflex
 ○ Measuring angles
 ○ Angles at a point and on a straight line
 ○ Alternate and corresponding angles

Enlargements
  ○ Scale factor and centre of enlargement

● **The class can now do Exercise 12E from Pupil Book 2.**

Exercise 12E Answers

1 a 21 cm² **b** 7.5 cm² **c** 21 cm²
2 a A – Acute, B – Obtuse, C – Acute, D – Right-angled, E – Reflex, F – Obtuse
 b Smaller because CD is parallel to AB and CB is not parallel to AF
3

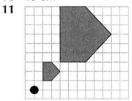

4 a

	0	1	2	3	4
1		A			
2	F		B,C,D		
3				G	
4					E

 b Rectangle or Rhombus

5 $a = 54°$, $b = 82°$, $c = 152°$
6 a 288 cm² **b** 4 **c** 1:16
7 a 80 km **b** no, 100 kph ≈ 62 mph
 c 93 miles, 50 km is about 31 and 3 × 31 = 93
8 a check sides measure 5 cm, 8 cm and 7 cm **b** 82°
9 a $a = 39°$, $b = 39°$, $c = 43°$ **b** angle ADB = angle DBE so AD is parallel to BE
10 40 cm
11

12 a 6.32 cm **b** 5.66 cm

Plenary

● Go through the answers to the exercise. Discuss and clarify those with which
  students had difficulty.

Homework

1 Find the area of a kite with a long diagonal of 10 cm and a short diagonal of 6 cm.

2 Find the area of a circle with a radius of 3 cm.

Answers
 1 30 cm²
 2 28.3 cm²

LESSON 12.6

Framework objectives – Handling Data

Revision of Handling Data:

Interpret graphs and diagrams and draw inferences to support or cast doubt on initial conjectures; have a basic understanding of correlation.

Analyse data to find patterns and exceptions, look for cause and effect and try to explain anomalies.

Oral and mental starter

- The following is a 10-question, SATs-style mental test on the theme of Handling Data. Repeat each question twice and allow 10 seconds to answer.

  1 An ordinary, fair, six-sided dice is rolled. What is the probability that the dice shows an odd number?

  2 What is the mean of these numbers? [Write 10, 10 and 25 on the board.]

  3 The pictogram shows the number of trains that go from Barnsley to Leeds and Huddersfield per day.
  How many more trains go to Leeds than to Huddersfield?

Leeds	◇◇◇◇
Huddersfield	◇◇◁

  ◇ = 4 trains

  4 What is the range of these numbers? [Write on the board: 4, 8, 2, 9, 7, 12, 1, 3, 7, 8, 2 and 3.]

  5 A dance class contains both boys and girls. The probability that a member of the class, picked at random, is a girl is 0.7. What is the probability that a member picked at random is a boy?

  6 A bag contains only red, blue and green balls. The table shows the probability of choosing each colour, when a ball is picked from the bag at random. [Draw the table shown.]
  What is the probability that the ball picked is blue *or* green?

Red	Blue	Green
0.35	0.2	0.45

  7 An ordinary, fair, six-sided dice is rolled. What is the probability that the dice shows a score of 7?

  8 Two ordinary, fair, six-sided dice are rolled. What is the probability that the total score is 3?

  9 What is the median of these numbers? [Write on the board: 7, 8, 10, 13, 15 and 20.]

  10 The table shows the number of pets owned by ten students. How many pets are owned altogether?

Number of pets	Frequency
1	2
2	5
3	3

  Answers **1** 0.5 **2** 15 **3** 6 **4** 11 **5** 0.3 **6** 0.65 **7** 0
  8 $\frac{2}{36} = \frac{1}{18}$ **9** 11.5 **10** 21

Main lesson activity

- This is a revision lesson on Handling Data.
- The questions in the Pupil Book exercise are graded from Level 4 to Level 7 as follows:

  Q. 1, 2   **Level 4**
  Q. 3, 4, 5, 6   **Level 5**
  Q. 7, 8, 10, 11   **Level 6**
  Q. 9   **Level 7**

- Before letting students start the questions you can go through key points (as suggested below) or discuss some specific questions with the class to remind them of the methods used.

Probability
  ○ Language and definition of probability
  ○ Writing probabilities as fractions, decimals or percentages
  ○ Sample space diagrams

Averages
  ○ The three averages used for discrete data
  ○ Range of a set of data
  ○ Mean of a table of discrete data

Surveys
- ○ Methods of sampling
- ○ Unbiased questions with unambiguous response boxes

Scatter diagrams
- ○ Types of correlation
- ○ Using line of best fit for predicting values

- **The class can now do Exercise 12F from Pupil Book 2.**

Exercise 12F Answers

1 **a** $\frac{1}{2}$ **b** (H,1),(H,2),(H,3),(H,4),(H,5),(H,6),(T,1),(T,2),(T,3),(T,4),(T,5),(T,6) **c** $\frac{1}{6}$

2 **a** $\frac{3}{16}$ **b** $\frac{6}{16} = \frac{3}{8}$

   c i **ii** 1

   Score on first dice

	1	**2**	**3**	**4**
1	1	2	3	4
2	2	4	6	8
3	3	6	9	12
4	4	8	12	16

Score on second dice

3 Any combination where the number of red to blue is in the ratio 2:1, e.g. 20 red 10 blue

4 **a** 2 **b** 3 **c** 4

5 **a** Q **b** R **c** P and R

6 **a** 6 **b** 5 **c i** False, there is no mode to start with **ii** False, both old and new marks were above median **iii** True, total will be 2 more

7 0.3

8 **a** Not representative **b** Overlap of responses

9 **a** $3x$ **b** $3x + 1$

10 The percentage value of a car decreases as the mileage increases or there is a negative correlation **b** 50% **c** 30 000 miles

11 **a** 30 **b** 4.9

Plenary

- Go through the answers to the exercise. Discuss and clarify those with which students had difficulty.

Homework

1 Robyn has 6 cards with numbers on them. Find the range, mode, median and mean of the numbers.

   | 3 | 7 | 7 | 6 | 5 | 2 |

2 When two dice are rolled the probability of a double one is 1/36.

   a When two dice are rolled what is the probability of a double 2?

   b Circle the answer that shows the probability of a treble six when three dice are rolled.

   $\frac{1}{18}$ $\frac{1}{216}$ $\frac{3}{216}$ $\frac{1}{42}$

Answers

1 Range = 5, Mode = 7, Median = 5.5, Mean = 5

2 **a** $\frac{1}{36}$ **b** $\frac{1}{216}$

THIS IS A NON-CALCULATOR PAPER

THIS IS THE START OF THE TIER 4–6 PAPER

1 The T-shapes below are made from small cubes.

(a) Write how many small cubes there are in this T-shape.

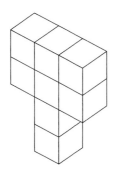

Number of cubes: ....

1 mark

(b) How many **more** small cubes are there in this T-shape?

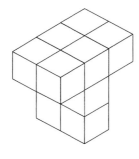

Number of cubes: ....

1 mark

2 Find the answers.

(a) 826 − 352 =

....

1 mark

(b) 42 × 7 =

....

1 mark

(c) 225 ÷ 9 =

....

1 mark

3 (a) A grocer sells melons for £1.50 each.

What is the cost of 12 melons?

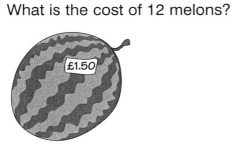

£ ....

(b) The grocer sells raspberries at £1.75 for a punnet.

What is the cost of 4 punnets?

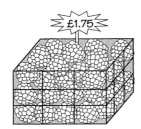

£ ....

1 mark

(c) How many punnets of raspberries can you buy with £10?

....

1 mark

(d) The grocer has a special offer of two punnets for £2.99.

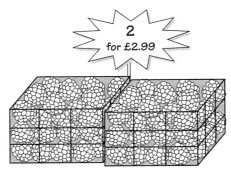

How many punnets can you buy with £15?

....

1 mark

(e) What is the greatest number of punnets you can buy with £8?

4 In a magic square, each row, column and diagonal adds up to the same number.

For example, each row, column and diagonal in this magic square adds up to 15.

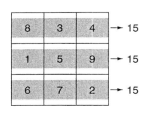
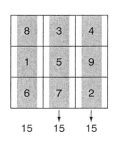
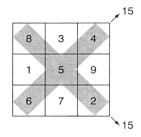

Here is another magic square.

Use the numbers in the first row of this magic square to work out what each row, column and diagonal must add up to.

Then complete the magic square.

44	18	34
22	32	....
....	....	20

44 + 18 + 34 =

....

1 mark

3 marks

134   © HarperCollins*Publishers* Ltd 2003

5 (a) Complete the table.

1 kg	=	.... g
....	=	1500 g
125 g × 10	=	.... kg .... g

3 marks

(b) 1.5 kg of flour costs 85p.

How much will 4.5 kg flour cost?

£ ....

1 mark

THIS IS THE START OF THE TIER 5–7 PAPER

6 A 3 × 3 × 3 cube is made from 27 different coloured small cubes.

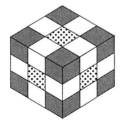

The small cubes with 3 faces showing are coloured grey.

The small cubes with 2 faces showing are coloured white.

The small cubes with 1 face showing are dotted.

The small cubes with 0 faces showing are striped.

(a) Complete the table below to show the number of small cubes of each colour that are used.

Grey cubes ....

White cubes ....

Dotted cubes ....

Striped cubes ....

Total: 27

3 marks

(b) A 4 × 4 × 4 cube is made in the same way. Complete the table below to show the number of small cubes of each type it has and the total number of cubes used.

Grey cubes ....

White cubes ....

Dotted cubes ....

Striped cubes 8

Total: ....

2 marks

7 This is how Helen works out 25% of 240 in her head.

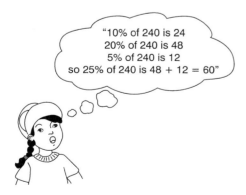

"10% of 240 is 24
20% of 240 is 48
5% of 240 is 12
so 25% of 240 is 48 + 12 = 60"

(a) Show how Helen can work out 25% of 180 in her head.

2 marks

(b) This is how Jim works out 25% of 240 in his head.

"50% of 240 is 120
so 25% of 240 is 60"

Show how Jim can work out 25% of 460 in his head.

2 marks

8 (a) A school needs 250 pencils.

The pencils come in packs of 12.

How many packs must the school order?

Show your working.

.... packs

2 marks

(b) Rulers cost 22p each.

How much do 250 rulers cost?

Show your working. Give your answer in pounds.

£ ....

3 marks

9 (a) There are n cubes in this tower.

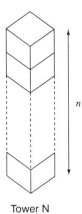

Tower N

Linda adds another 7 cubes to the tower.

Write an expression to show the total number of cubes in Linda's tower.

....
1 mark

(b) Qayser builds another tower.

This tower is m cubes high.

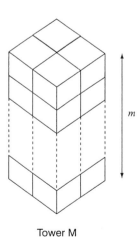

Tower M

Write an expression to show the total number of cubes in Qayser's tower.

....
1 mark

(c)

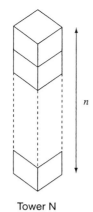

Tower N

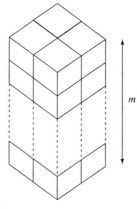

Tower M

The number of cubes in each tower is the same.

Which expression below is true?

Put a tick (✓) by the correct expression.

$n = m \times 2$	
$n = m \times 4$	
$n = m \div 2$	
$n = m \div 4$	

1 mark

(d) Brian builds two more towers like Tower N and Tower M. Brian's towers have equal number of cubes in them, and their heights are related by this expression:
$n = m + 6$.

Work out the value of m.

$m = $ ....

1 mark

10 The graphs below show the number of goals scored per match by Team A and Team B over 50 games.

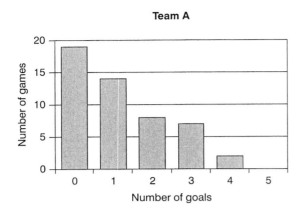

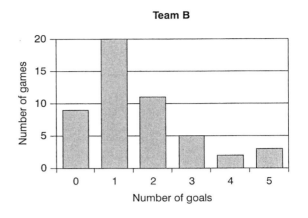

(a) How many goals did Team A score altogether in the 50 games?

Goals: ....

2 marks

(b) Which team scored three or more goals in 20% of their games?

Explain your answer.

2 marks

(c) Eli says that the graphs show that Team B is more successful than Team A.

Give a reason why this may not be true.

1 mark

11 Three people A, B and C run a race.

Below are five different distance–time graphs.

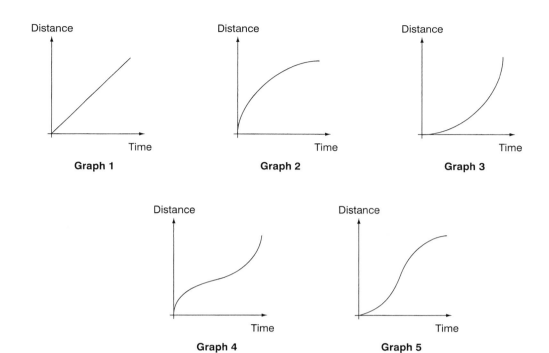

Fill in the gaps below to show which runner matches up with one of the graphs.

Runner A sets off quickly, slows down and then speeds up

Graph ....

Runner B runs at a steady speed

Graph ....

Runner C sets off quickly and then slows down

Graph ....

3 marks

12 Use the graphs to match each line with its equation.

The first one has been done for you.

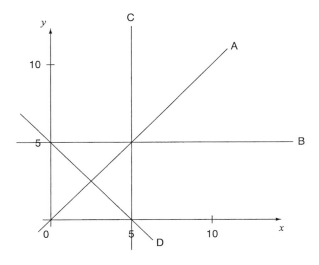

LINE A ← y = x

x = 5

LINE B

y = 5

LINE C

x + y = 5

LINE D

y = 5x

13 Each shape in this question has an area of 20 cm².

No diagram is drawn to scale.

(a) Calculate the length of the base of the parallelogram.

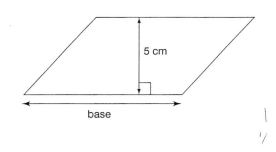

5 cm

base

area = 20 cm²   base = ... cm

(b) Calculate the height of the triangle.

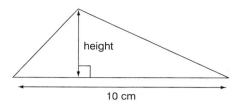

area = 20 cm^2

height = ... cm

1 mark

(c) What is the value of h in this trapezium?

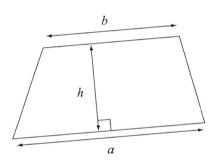

area = 20 cm^2 $a + b = 4$ cm

h = ... cm

1 mark

A different trapezium has an area of 20 cm^2 and a height of 5 cm. What is the value of $a + b$ in the trapezium?

area = 20 cm^2 $h = 5$ cm

$a + b =$ .... cm

1 mark

(d) Look at this rectangle:

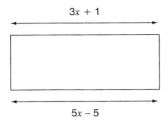

3x + 1

5x − 5

area = 20 cm²

Calculate the value of x and use it to find the perimeter of the rectangle.

Show your working.

perimeter = ... cm

2 marks

14 This is a series of patterns with black and white squares.

Pattern Number 1   Pattern Number 2   Pattern Number 3

 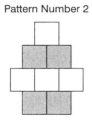 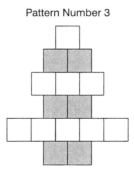

(a) Complete this table:

pattern number	number of black squares	number of white squares
5		
12		

2 marks

(b) Complete this table by writing expressions:

pattern number	expression for the number of black squares	expression for the number of white squares
n		

2 marks

(c) Write an expression to show the total number of tiles in pattern number n.

Simplify your expression.

....

1 mark

(d) A different series of patterns is made with squares.

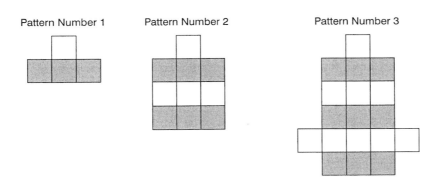

Pattern Number 1   Pattern Number 2   Pattern Number 3

For this series of patterns, write an expression to show the total number of tiles in pattern number n. Show your working and simplify your expression.

....

2 marks

15 (a) Each of these calculations has the same answer, 75.

Fill in each gap with a number.

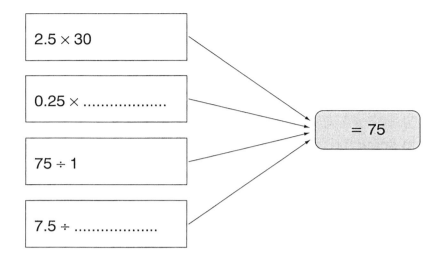

2.5 × 30

0.25 × ....

75 ÷ 1

7.5 ÷ ....

= 75

2 marks

(b) Solve these equations to find the values of a, b and c.

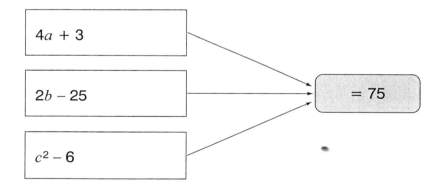

$4a + 3$

$2b - 25$

$c^2 - 6$

= 75

$a = $ .... $b = $ .... $c = $ ....

3 marks

THIS IS THE END OF THE TIER 4–6 PAPER

16 In the scale drawing, the shaded area represents a rectangular flowerbed.

There is a path all around the flowerbed.

The shortest distance from the flowerbed to the edge of the path is always 2 m.

On the diagram, draw accurately the position of the edge of the path.

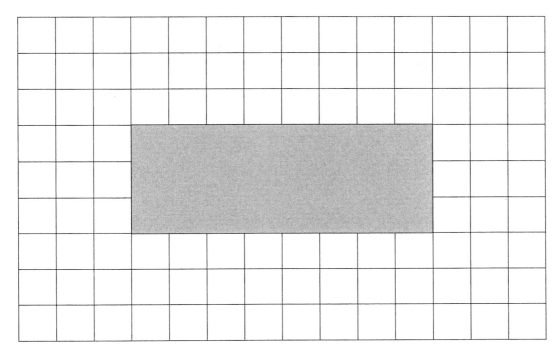

Scale: 1 cm to 1 m

2 marks

17 This is what a student wrote:

$$\frac{a}{2} + \frac{b}{3} = \frac{a + b}{5}$$

Show that the student was wrong.

2 marks

18 Passengers have been complaining to a bus company about how long they have to wait for a bus.

An inspector records the waiting times of 100 passengers on one of the company's bus routes on one day.

Results

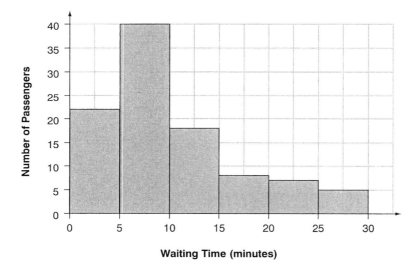

Waiting Time (minutes)

(a) Use the graph to estimate the probability that a passenger chosen at random will wait for 15 minutes or longer.

....

1 mark

(b) Use the graph to estimate the probability that a customer chosen at random will wait for 7.5 minutes or less.

....

1 mark

(c) Calculate an estimate of the mean waiting time per passenger.

Show your working.

You may complete the table below to help you with the calculation.

Waiting time (minutes)	Mid-point of bar (x)	Number of passengers (f)	fx
0–	2.5	22	
5–			
10–			
15–			
20–			
25–30			

.... minutes

2 marks

(d) The inspector wants to improve the survey.

She records the waiting times of more customers.

Give a different way the inspector could improve the survey.

1 mark

19 (a) Find the values of a and b when $p = 5$

$$a = \frac{2p^3}{5}$$

$a =$ ....

1 mark

$$b = \frac{p^2(p + 1)}{3p}$$

$b =$ ....

1 mark

(b) Simplify this expression as fully as possible:

$$\frac{15cd}{3d}$$

....

1 mark

(c) Multiply out and simplify this expression:

$$3(x + 4) - 2(3 - 2x)$$

....

1 mark

Handling Data 3

Framework objectives – Revision of statistical techniques

Discuss how data relate to a problem; identify possible sources, including primary and secondary sources.

Find summary values that represent the raw data, and select the statistics most appropriate to the problem.

Oral and mental starter

- The class should work in small groups for this activity.
- Explain to the class that the lesson will be used to revise handling data topics that they have already covered, in preparation for an investigation next lesson. Tell the class that this activity is called 'The A–to–Z of handling data'.
- Ask each group to think of as many handling data topics and words beginning with different letters of the alphabet as they can, excluding those to do with probability. You may wish to ask for a few suggestions and write them on the board, such as average, bias, data, graph, etc.
- Ask the groups to write down an example for each word they come up with. For example: the **average** of 2 and 4 is 3.
- Give the groups a few minutes to discuss their answers then ask the groups to give you the topics to write on the board, covering the meaning of each one.

Main lesson activity

- Continuing from the oral and mental starter, ask the students to give you responses to the following types of questions.

  1 What sort of things should you think about when planning a question and response section for a questionnaire?
  2 What is a census?
  3 Name some ways of recording data.
  4 What is the difference between primary and secondary data?
  5 How can you choose a random sample from a group of people?
  6 What is a two-way table?
  7 What is a frequency table?
  8 Name as many different types of frequency diagrams as you can.
  9 What is a stem–and–leaf diagram?
  10 How do you work out a mode, a median, a mean and a range for a set of data?

- You should look for answers which refer to the following.
  1 Avoid: leading question; missing or overlapping responses; any form of bias.
  2 A census is a survey of a whole population.
  3 Tally chart, data collection sheet or observation sheet.
  4 Primary data is data obtained directly by the person carrying out the research whereas secondary data has already been collected by someone else.
  5 A random sample of a group could be obtained by putting everyone's name in a bag, then drawing a portion of the names out.
  6 A two-way table records two sets of related information within one table, for example make of car and colour of car.
  7 A frequency table is a table showing the number of times (frequency) that each particular value or item is recorded in a survey or experiment.
  8 Pictogram, bar chart, pie chart, line graph, frequency polygon, histogram.
  9 A stem–and–leaf diagram is an ordered set of numerical data, grouped to show how the data is distributed. It is in effect a bar chart using a list of numerical data.
  10 The mode is the most common value; the median is the middle value of an ordered set of data; the mean is the total of all the values divided by the number of items of data; the range is the difference between the largest and smallest values.

- Ask the class to look through the table of vocabulary in the Pupil Book, to make sure they are familiar with the terms there.

- **The class can now do Exercise 13A from Pupil Book 2.**

1 a Other categories not given, e.g. 'cycle' or 'other'   **b** The classes overlap
  c 8.15 AM is in two categories

2 a

	Boys	Girls
$12 \leqslant T < 14$	2	2
$14 \leqslant T < 16$	4	1
$16 \leqslant T < 18$	3	2
$18 \leqslant T < 20$	0	4
$20 \leqslant T < 22$	1	1

b 45%
c $18 \leqslant T < 20$
d $14 \leqslant T < 16$

3 a
```
0 | 5  6  8  9
1 | 0  1  1  2  2  4  4  5  6  6  7  8  9  9
2 | 0
```
Key 0 | 6 means 6 students

  b 14   **c** 15   **d** 8

4 a There are longer bars for females over 55 years old.
  b Females may live longer generally in France; more men than women were killed
     in WWII (and WWI).

5 a mode = 1, median = 4, mean = 11.7   **b** mode = 5, median = 5, mean = 5.4
  c mode = £4.50, median = £3.50, mean = £3.41
  d mode = 18, median = 20, mean = 20.8

6 a Check that pie chart shows the following data:
  b For this to be true the classes would have to
     have equal numbers of students in.

Class	A	B	C	D
Angle (°)	72	54	144	90

The vertical axis (population) starts at 56 500 000, making population appear to more
than double in ten years. In fact it has only risen by about 2.4% as stated.

Plenary

- Explain to the class that it is important to be able to draw appropriate statistical diagrams and calculate statistics such as averages, but that it is equally important to be able to interpret them, commenting on how useful they are.
- Ask the class if it is appropriate to use a pie chart to represent 20 categories of data [with so many categories, a bar chart might be easier to interpret], or ask the class if it is sensible to use a scatter graph for 5 pairs of data [there are probably not enough data to produce a meaningful graph].
- Briefly refer to the mode, median and mean and explain the effect of an extreme value on the mean. Use the phrase, 'it would be inappropriate to use the mean as one value has distorted the data'. For example, the data 50, 50, 50, 50, 100 give a mean of 50 when the 100 is excluded, but a mean of 60 when the 100 is included.

Homework

1 The weights (in kg) of 24 men are given below.

62	48	55	67	81	40	45	59	58	62
72	65	70	82	66	48	59	68	71	65
54	57	76	74						

b In which class is the median weight?
c Represent this information in a pie chart.
d Explain why these weights are not
   representative of the whole adult population.

a Use the data to copy and complete the
   frequency table.

Weight, W (kg)	Tally	Frequency
$40 \leqslant W < 50$		
$50 \leqslant W < 60$		
$60 \leqslant W < 70$		
$70 \leqslant W < 80$		
$80 \leqslant W < 90$		

2 These tables show the average monthly temperatures for Paris and Madrid over the course of one year.

Paris

	Jan	Feb	Mar	Apr	May	Jun	Jul	Aug	Sep	Oct	Nov	Dec
°C	3.7	3.7	7.3	9.7	13.7	16.5	19.0	18.7	16.1	12.5	7.3	5.2

Madrid

	Jan	Feb	Mar	Apr	May	Jun	Jul	Aug	Sep	Oct	Nov	Dec
°C	5.3	6.7	9.7	12.0	16.1	20.8	24.6	23.9	20.5	14.7	9.3	6.0

a Draw suitable graphs to represent both sets of data.
b Comment on the differences between the average monthly temperatures in Paris and Madrid.

Answers

1 a

Weight, W (kg)	Tally	Frequency
$40 \leqslant W < 50$	IIII	4
$50 \leqslant W < 60$	HHT I	6
$60 \leqslant W < 70$	HHT II	7
$70 \leqslant W < 80$	HHT	5
$80 \leqslant W < 90$	II	2

c Check pie chart has these angles:

Weight, W (kg)	Angle (°)
$40 \leqslant W < 50$	60
$50 \leqslant W < 60$	90
$60 \leqslant W < 70$	105
$70 \leqslant W < 80$	75
$80 \leqslant W < 90$	30

b $60 \leqslant W < 70$
d Only males in results.
2 a Histograms or line graphs drawn.   **b** Average temperatures consistently higher in Madrid.

Framework objectives – A handling data project

Select, construct and modify, on paper and using ICT, suitable graphical representation to progress an enquiry.

Interpret graphs and diagrams and draw inferences to support or cast doubt on initial conjectures; have a basic understanding of correlation.

Communicate interpretations and results of a statistical enquiry using selected tables, graphs and diagrams in support, using ICT as appropriate.

Solve substantial problems by breaking them into simpler tasks, using a range of efficient techniques, methods and resources, including ICT.

Oral and mental starter

- Write on the board, 'A solo pop singer is more likely to be female than male, but a singer in a band is more likely to be male than female.'
- Ask the class how they could investigate this.
- Answers which they might say or be prompted to say could include:
    Make a list of known singers and bands
    Do a survey using the pop charts
- You could discuss the fact that the chart data will only look at the most successful singers and therefore may give a biased result. You could then suggest that the initial hypothesis needs to say that it refers to the most successful singers.

Main lesson activity

- The activities given in this section could easily take two lessons, depending on the amount of detail asked for when carrying out the investigation. You may wish to ask the students to collect certain data prior to the lesson, or you may decide to provide the students with secondary data.
- Continuing from the oral and mental starter, show the class the handling data cycle and the related checklist for completing a handling data investigation, on p. 188 of Pupil Book 2. The list is also reproduced opposite.
- Go through and consider how each point applies to the pop singers example from the oral and mental starter:
    ○ **[Statement of topic]** Compare number of male singers and female singers in the charts.
    ○ **[Hypothesis]** 'In the charts, a solo singer is more likely to be female than male, but a singer in a band is more likely to be male than female.'
    ○ **[Sample size]** Look at, say, the top 50.
    ○ **[Foreseen problems]** Charts will change from week to week – may need to use charts over several weeks.
    ○ **[How to obtain data]** Use pop charts from different sources (this information could be obtained from the Internet).
    ○ **[Data collection sheet]** Record the number of bands and the number of solo artists, record the number of males and females in each case.
    ○ **[Analysis]** Calculate average numbers per week. Represent in percentage bars or pie charts.
    ○ **[Factors affecting results]** Songs stay in the charts for several weeks, so the weeks looked at should really be far apart in the year, rather than consecutive.
    ○ **[Conclusion]** State whether you agree with initial hypothesis based on your results.

- **The class can now do one of the investigations in Exercise 13B from Pupil Book 2, working in small groups.**

Plenary

- Having observed the students working on a choice of investigations, you may wish to give one or more groups the opportunity to present their findings so far to the rest of the class.

Checklist for completing a handling data investigation
- **Specify the problem and plan**
  - ○ statement of problem or topic to investigate
  - ○ hypothesis stating what you think the investigation will show
  - ○ how you will choose your sample and sample size
  - ○ any practical problems you foresee
  - ○ how you will obtain your data, possibly including how to avoid bias
- **Collect data from a variety of sources**
  - ○ follow initial plan and use a suitable data-collection sheet
- **Process and represent data**
  - ○ analysis of your results using appropriate statistical calculations and diagrams
- **Interpret and discuss data**
  - ○ comparison of results with your original hypothesis
  - ○ list of any factors which might have affected your results and how you could overcome these in future
  - ○ a final conclusion

Homework

Choose one of the following tasks.

1 Complete the investigation started in the lesson by writing up the report.

2 Collect data in order to investigate the pop singers example.

3 Carry out and write up a detailed investigation of your own choice.

Shape, Space and Measures 4

Framework objectives – Shape and space revision

Use units of measurement to calculate and solve problems in a variety of contexts.

Know and use the formulae for the circumference and area of a circle.

Calculate the surface area and volume of right prisms.

Oral and mental starter

- The class should work in pairs or small groups for this activity.
- Tell them that they are going to revise perimeter, area and volume, which they have already covered.
- Ask each pair or group to write down the formulae for the perimeter and the area of any 2-D shapes.
- Now ask each pair or group to write down the formulae for the surface area and the volume of any 3-D shapes.
- Give the class a few minutes to discuss their answers.

Main lesson activity

- Once the class has finished writing down the formulae, ask individual students to draw a shape on the board or OHT and below it give the formula for its perimeter, area or volume.
- Continue this activity until all the shapes are covered.
- **The class can now do Exercise 14A from Pupil Book 2.**

Plenary

- Tell the class that in the next lesson they will be working on a shape and space investigation, and that they may need to use some of the formulae which they met during the present lesson.

Key Words
- area
- circumference
- surface area
- volume

Homework

1 Find the area of each of the following shapes.

a    5 cm   9 cm

b   8 cm   6 cm

c 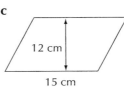   12 cm   15 cm

d 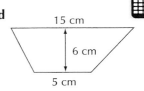   15 cm   6 cm   5 cm

2 Calculate **i** the circumference and **ii** the area of each of the following circles. Take π = 3.14 or use the π key on your calculator. Give your answers to one decimal place.

a   8 cm

b 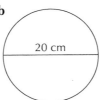   20 cm

3 Calculate the volume of this prism.

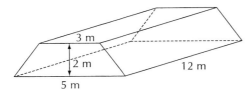
3 m   2 m   5 m   12 m

Answers
1 a 45 cm²   b 24 cm²   c 180 cm²   d 60 cm²
2 a i 50.3 cm   ii 201.1 cm²   b i 62.8 cm   ii 314.2 cm²
3 96 m³

Framework objectives – Shape and space investigation
Present a concise, reasoned argument, using symbols, diagrams and related explanatory text.

Oral and mental starter

- Ask individual students to give the formulae for the perimeter, the area or the volume of various 2-D and 3-D shapes.

Main lesson activity

- Each investigation given in this section will take up to two lessons to complete.
- The class can work in pairs or small groups. The whole class may undertake the same investigation, or pairs or groups may choose their own investigation from the four given.
- Before the investigations are started, briefly go through the methods of doing an investigation:
  ○ Draw some easy examples first, making all diagrams clear with all measurements shown.
  ○ Put your results in a table with suitable headings.
  ○ Look for any patterns among the entries in the table.
  ○ Describe and explain any patterns which you spot.
  ○ Try to find a rule or formula to explain each pattern.
  ○ Try another example to see whether your rule or formula does work.
  ○ Summarise your results with a conclusion.
  ○ If possible, extend the investigation by introducing different questions.
- Note: the students may need centimetre-squared paper.
- **The class can now do Exercise 14B from Pupil Book 2.**

Exercise 14B Answers

The layout below for each investigation is minimal. The students should always explain their choice of presentation and link all their diagrams with the text. They may use different approaches to the investigations and these should be noted. The use of algebra would also enhance the students' work and should be encouraged wherever possible. All the investigations are helpful to the preparation for the GCSE coursework assessment.

1 It is expected that the students will draw a sequence of squares and complete a table similar to the one on the right. Note that units are not necessary for this investigation.

Size of square	1×1	2×2	3×3	4×4	5×5
Perimeter (*P*)	4	8	12	16	20
Area (*A*)	1	4	9	16	25

From the table, the students will notice that the 4×4 square has the same value for its perimeter and area. They should see that this is the only solution, by noticing that, after the 4×4 square, the area is always greater than the perimeter. They should then check this using another example. (It could also be shown by drawing a graph.)

Some students may be able to show that this is the only solution by using an algebraic approach.

For a square of side l, $P = 4l$ and $A = l^2$.
For the square to have the same value for P and A, $4l = l^2$.
This is true only for $l = 0$ or $l = 4$. Clearly, $l = 0$ has no meaning, so $l = 4$ is the only solution.

To extend the investigation, the students could consider rectangles.

By drawing a number of rectangles, they should find that the value of the perimeter equals the value of the area when $l = 6$ and $w = 3$.

They may think that this is the only solution, but intuition may tell them that other solutions may exist. For completeness, this can be shown by an algebraic approach:

For a rectangle of length l and width w, $P = 2l + 2w$ and $A = lw$.
For the rectangle to have the same value for P and A, $2l + 2w = lw$, which gives:

$$lw - 2w = 2l$$
$$w(l - 2) = 2l$$
$$w = \frac{2l}{l - 2}$$

This shows that there are an infinite number of solutions. For example, when $l = 10$, $w = 2.5$. Other solutions can now be found.
Considering circles would also extend the investigation.

2 The students should start by completing a table of results to show the length (l), perimeter (P) and area (A) of the squares. They can then find the ratios $l:P$ and $l:A$.

From the table, the students can see that the ratio $l:P$ is always 1:4 and the ratio $l:A$ is 1:n, where n is the length of the side of the square. They should now test their rules on new data.

Size of square	l	P	A	$l:P$	$l:A$
1×1	1	4	1	1:4	1:1
2×2	2	8	4	1:4	1:2
3×3	3	12	9	1:4	1:3

They may be able to generalise: for a square of size $n \times n$, $l:P = 1:4$ and $l:A = 1:n$.

The investigation could be extended by looking at cubes and considering the ratio of the length of a side to the surface area and the ratio of the length of a side to the volume.

3 The students should start by considering squares of different sizes. They will realise that it will be easier to use even numbers for the side of the square. They should then present their results in a table, as shown below, giving their final answers to a suitable degree of accuracy. (One decimal place is suggested.)

Size of square	Area of square	Area of coin	Area of coin as % of area of square	% waste
2 cm × 2 cm	4 cm^2	3.14 cm^2	78.5%	21.5%
4 cm × 4 cm	16 cm^2	12.57 cm^2	78.5%	21.5%
6 cm × 6 cm	36 cm^2	28.27 cm^2	78.5%	21.5%

The students should now see that the percentage waste is always 21.5% for squares of any size. A further example would show this.

An algebraic approach could also be used. For a square of side $2r$, the area of the square is $4r^2$ and the area of the coin is πr^2.

The area of the coin as a percentage of the area of the square is:

$$\frac{\pi r^2}{4r^2} \times 100 = \frac{\pi}{4} \times 100 = 78.5$$

So, the percentage waste is 21.5%.

The investigation could be extended to four coins stamped from a square or by considering rectangular sheets of metal.

4 a For a 6 × 2 table, there are two bounces.
  b For a 6 × 2 table, the ball goes down pocket C.
  c After drawing different sized tables, including square tables, the students should complete a table to show their results. The table on the right shows some results for 17 different tables, with the ball always starting from pocket A.

  From the table, the students should be able to spot various patterns. For example: a square table has no bounces and the ball ends up in pocket C; when the length and width of the table are reversed, the number of bounces is the same but the ball may not end up in the same pocket.

  The following is a summary.
  - For a table of length l and width w, write it as the ratio $l:w$.
  - When $l:w$ cannot be simplified, the number of bounces, N, is given by the formula:
    $N = l + w - 2$
  - When $l:w$ can be simplified to give the ratio $a:b$, the number of bounces, N, is given by the formula:
    $N = a + b - 2$
  - When l and w (or a and b if simplified) are both odd, the ball ends up in pocket C.
  - When only l is odd (or a if simplified), the ball ends up in pocket D.
  - If only l is even (or a if simplified), the ball ends up in pocket B.

  The students may write down these conditions, but in all cases they should test their rules or formulae on further examples.

Size of table	Number of bounces	Pocket
1×1	0	C
2×2	0	C
3×3	0	C
2×1	1	B
3×1	2	C
4×1	3	B
3×2	3	D
4×2	1	B
5×2	5	D
6×2	2	C
4×3	5	B
5×3	6	C
6×3	1	B
2×3	3	B
3×4	5	D
3×5	6	C
3×6	1	D

Plenary

- Having observed the students working on the investigations, you may wish to discuss one of their choices.

Key Words

- investigate
- generalise

Homework

Complete the investigation you started in the lesson.

Framework objectives – Symmetry revision

Visualise and use 2-D representations of 3-D objects.

Use rotations and reflections on paper. Identify reflection symmetry in 3-D shapes.

Oral and mental starter

- The class should work in pairs or small groups for this activity.
- Tell them that they are going to revise reflection and rotational symmetry, which they have already covered.
- Ask each pair or group to draw and write down the names of any 2-D shapes, and then to draw on them all the lines of symmetry.
- Now ask them to repeat the activity but to write down the **order of rotational symmetry** below each one. Give the class a few minutes to discuss their answers.
- Then ask them to write down how to find the number of planes of symmetry for a 3-D shape.

Main lesson activity

- Once the class have finished writing down their answers, ask individual students to draw a shape on the board or OHT and to insert its lines of symmetry or to give its order of rotational symmetry.
- Continue this activity until it is clear that the class understand the concepts.
- Briefly remind them how to find the number of planes of symmetry for a 3-D shape by showing them that a cuboid has three planes of symmetry.

- **The class can now do Exercise 14C from Pupil Book 2.**

1 **a** 2 **b** 2 **c** 6 **d** 4 **e** 5
2 **a** 2 **b** 1 **c** 1 **d** 4
3 **a** 2 **b** 2 **c** 5 **d** 4 **e** 2
4 **a** 4 **b** 3 **c** 4 **d** 2
5 **a** 2 **b** 3 **c** 2 **d** 3
6 Cuboid with two square faces

Plenary

Key Words

- Tell the class that in the next lesson they will be working on a symmetry investigation and that they may need to use some of the concepts which they met during the present lesson.

☐ **reflection symmetry**
☐ **rotational symmetry**
☐ **plane of symmetry**

Homework

Design a logo for a badge for your school, which has both reflection and rotational symmetry.

Framework objectives – Symmetry investigation

Present a concise, reasoned argument, using symbols, diagrams and related explanatory text.

Oral and mental starter

- Ask individual students to explain reflection symmetry, rotational symmetry and planes of symmetry.

Main lesson activity

- Each investigation given in this section will probably take two lessons.
- The class can work in pairs or groups and the class can all work on the same investigation or be allowed to make their own choice from the four investigations given.
- Before the class start the investigation, briefly go through the methods of doing an investigation:
  - Draw some easy examples first, showing any lines of symmetry and/or stating the order of rotational symmetry on the diagrams.
  - Explain anything you notice from the diagrams.
  - Describe and explain any patterns which you spot.
  - Summarise your results with a conclusion.
  - If possible, extend the investigation by introducing different questions.
  - Note: the students may need tracing paper, mirrors, centimetre-squared paper and a selection of 3-D solids.
- **The class can now do Exercise 14D from Pupil Book 2.**

Exercise 14D Answers

The layout below for each investigation is minimal. The students should always explain their choice of presentation and link all their diagrams with the text. They may use different approaches to the investigations and these should be noted. The use of algebra would also enhance the students' work and should be encouraged wherever possible. All the investigations are helpful to the preparation for the GCSE coursework assessment.

1 It is expected that the students will draw diagrams to show the number of lines of symmetry for a tile with different numbers of shaded squares. Examples are shown below. (Reflections and rotations are omitted.)

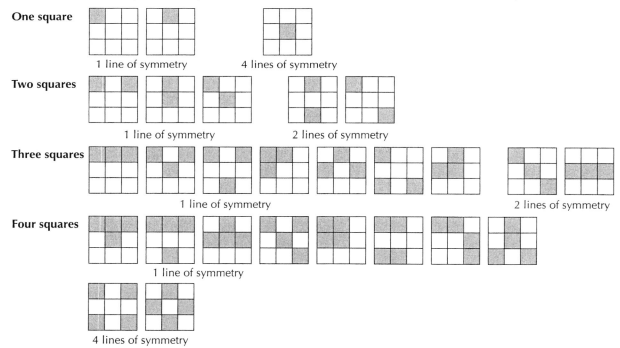

The students should now notice that for five shaded squares, the diagrams are the same as for four squares but with the shading reversed. Similarly for six, seven and eight squares. This could now be usefully summarised in a table.

The investigation could be extended by using a different size of tile.

2   There are 12 different pentominoes (excluding mirror images). The students should be encouraged to show their results in a table.

Pentomino						
Number of lines of symmetry	4	2	1	1	1	1
Order of rotational symmetry	4	2	1	1	1	1

Pentomino						
Number of lines of symmetry	0	0	0	0	0	0
Order of rotational symmetry	2	1	1	1	1	1

For students who extend the investigation, there are 35 different hexominoes.

3   Allowing rotations, the T-shape will fit in the 3 × 3 grid four times.

The students should now draw square grids of different sizes and find the number of ways in which the T-shape fits inside each grid. The table below shows the number of ways for three different square grids.

Size of grid	3 × 3	4 × 4	5 × 5
Number of ways	4	16	36

The students should now be able to spot the rule: the numbers of ways give the even square numbers. They should test another example to confirm that the rule works.

The students may also be able to use algebra in this investigation and arrive at a formula.

For an $n \times n$ grid, the total number of ways, T, the T-shape will fit inside the grid is given by:

$T = 4(n - 2)^2$ for $n > 2$

To extend the investigation, the students could consider rectangular grids or use a different shape.

4   For this investigation, it is useful for the students to have access to a collection of different solids. The table below is not exhaustive.

3-D solid	Outline	Symmetry number
Cube	Square	24
Cuboid	Rectangle	4
Regular tetrahedron	Equilateral triangle	12
Square-based pyramid	Square	4
Regular octahedron	Square	4
Regular triangular prism	Equilateral triangle	6
Regular pentagonal prism	Regular pentagon	10
Regular hexagonal prism	Regular hexagon	12
Cylinder	Circle	∞
Sphere	Circle	∞

The students may notice that the symmetry number for any prism is twice the order of rotational symmetry for the cross-section of the prism.

Plenary

Key Words

- [ ] **investigate**
- [ ] **generalise**

- Having observed the students working on the investigations, you may wish to discuss one of their choices.

Homework

Complete the investigation you started in the lesson.

Handling Data 4

Framework objectives – Revision of probability

Use the vocabulary of probability in interpreting results involving uncertainty and prediction.

Identify all the mutually exclusive outcomes of an experiment; know that the sum of probabilities of all mutually exclusive outcomes is 1 and use this when solving problems.

Estimate probabilities from experimental data.

Compare experimental and theoretical probabilities in a range of contexts; appreciate the difference between mathematical explanation and experimental evidence.

Oral and mental starter

- The class should work in small groups for this activity.
- Explain to the class that the lesson will be used to revise the probability topics they have already covered, in preparation for an investigation next lesson.
- Ask the class a few simple probabilities. Ask the students to explain how they have worked each answer out. Some examples are given below
  - ○ rolling a 6 on a fair, six-sided dice
  - ○ rolling a 3 *or* a 4 on a fair, six-sided dice
  - ○ rolling an odd number on a fair, six-sided dice
  - ○ throwing a head on a fair coin
  - ○ picking a blue cube when there are 3 blue, 4 red and 3 green cubes in a bag
  - ○ *not* picking a blue cube in the above example
  - ○ it not raining, if the probability of rain is $\frac{3}{4}$

Main lesson activity

- Continuing from oral and mental starter, ask the students to give you responses to the following types of question.
  1 A box contains 60 sweets, of which 10 are strawberry.
    a What is the probability of picking a strawberry sweet?
    b What is the probability of picking a sweet that is not strawberry?
    c A second box of sweets of the same make contains 300 sweets. How many would you expect to be strawberry?
  2 A six-sided dice is rolled and lands on 6 four times out of 24 rolls. Do you think that the dice is fair? Give a reason.
  3 Two coins are thrown. How many different outcomes are there?
  4 What is the difference between theoretical and experimental probability?
  5 What could you do to test if a spinner is biased? 7 What are mutually exclusive events?
  6 What are independent events? 8 What are exhaustive events?
- You should look for answers which refer to the following.
  1 a $\frac{10}{60}$ or $\frac{1}{6}$ b $\frac{5}{6}$ c 50
  2 It appears biased as 6 out of 24 is $\frac{1}{4}$. If fair you would expect it to be close to $\frac{1}{6}$.
  3 Four, HH, HT, TH, TT
  4 Theoretical probability looks at equally likely outcomes whereas experimental probability is based on the results of an experiment or number of trials.
  5 Spin it many times and compare the results to see if the experimental probabilities are close to the theoretical probabilities based on the assumption that the spinner is fair.
  6 Independent events are events where the outcome of one event is not affected by the outcome of the other event and vice versa.
  7 Mutually exclusive events are events that cannot happen at the same time.
  8 Exhaustive events are events that cover every possible outcome.
- Ask the class to look through the table of vocabulary in the Pupil Book, to make sure they are familiar with the terms there.

- **The class can now do Exercise 15A from Pupil Book 2.**

1 a 8; HHH, HHT, HTH, THH, TTH, THT, HTT, TTT   **b** $\frac{1}{8}$ **c** $\frac{3}{8}$ **d** $\frac{7}{8}$
2 a 0.4   **b** 0.6
3 a $\frac{7}{50}$ **b** $\frac{12}{50} = \frac{6}{25}$ **c** $\frac{31}{50}$
4 a $\frac{6}{50}$ or 0.12   **b** $\frac{1}{5}$ or 0.2   **c** Probably not fair as the probabilities are quite different.
  d 30

Extension Answers

1 a Independent as 2nd roll is not affected by outcome of 1st roll.
  b Not independent – the chances of winning with 2nd ticket are increased as there is 1 ticket fewer to choose from.
  c Not independent
2 a Not mutually exclusive as 2 is both even and prime.
  b Mutually exclusive as the outcomes do not overlap.
  c Not mutually exclusive as 'at least one tail' includes 'two tails'.
3 a Exhaustive as all possible outcomes are included.
  b Not exhaustive as the outcome landing on the number 3 is not included.
  c Exhaustive as all possible outcomes are included.

Key Words

- event
- outcome
- random
- probability scale
- experimental probability
- theoretical probability
- relative frequency
- expectation
- bias
- fair
- sample
- sample space
- exhaustive
- independent
- mutually exclusive

Plenary

- Explain to the class that it is important to be able to calculate probabilities from experimental and theoretical situations in order to make and test hypotheses.
- Ask the class to explain the meaning of bias. Point out that bias can be tested either by looking at raw data or by comparing experimental and theoretical probabilities.
- As an example, show the class the table below, which gives the results of spinning a four-sided spinner 40 times. Ask the class if they think the spinner is biased, just by looking at these experimental frequencies.
- Now ask them to work out the theoretical probabilities and compare with experimental probabilities.

Number on spinner	1	2	3	4
Frequency	12	5	10	13

- From inspection of the data, the spinner appears to be biased against landing on 2, because this occurs much less than the other numbers. Comparison of the experimental with the theoretical probability verifies this conclusion (experimental = $\frac{5}{40}$ = 0.125; theoretical = $\frac{1}{4}$ = 0.25).
- Finally, point out that minor differences between expected frequencies and actual frequencies do not necessarily mean that there is bias.

Homework

Two four-sided spinners are each spun 80 times. The results are shown below.

For each spinner state whether you think it is biased by comparing **i** the individual frequencies **ii** the experimental and theoretical probabilities.

1st spinner

Number on spinner	1	2	3	4
Frequency	20	21	19	20

2nd spinner

Number on spinner	1	2	3	4
Frequency	25	17	16	22

Answers
The 1st spinner is probably not biased:
 i as the frequencies are all close to 20
 ii as the experimental probabilities are $\frac{20}{80}$ = 0.25, $\frac{21}{80}$ = 0.2625, $\frac{19}{80}$ = 0.2375, $\frac{20}{80}$ = 0.25, which are all close to the theoretical probability of 0.25.
The 2nd spinner is possibly biased:
 i as the frequencies are not close to 20
 ii as the experimental probabilities are $\frac{25}{80}$ = 0.3125, $\frac{17}{80}$ = 0.2125, $\frac{16}{80}$ = 0.2, $\frac{22}{80}$ = 0.275, which are not very close to the theoretical probability of 0.25. It could still be argued here that these are sufficiently close to 0.25 to suggest the spinner is fair.

Framework objectives – A probability investigation

Compare experimental evidence in a range of contexts; appreciate the difference between mathematical explanation and experimental evidence.

Oral and mental starter

- Write on the board, 'Teenagers are better at probability than adults'.
- Ask the class how they could investigate this.
- Students might suggest writing a set of probability questions to be given to both teenagers and adults. They could then record the results for their samples and compare the experimental probabilities of answering particular questions correctly for teenagers and adults.
- You could discuss how they would decide which people to use in the sample.

Main lesson activity

- The activities given in this section could easily take two lessons, depending on the amount of detail asked for when carrying out the investigation. You may wish to ask the students to collect certain data prior to the lesson or you may decide to provide the students with secondary data.
- Continuing from the oral and mental starter, show the class the handling data cycle and the related checklist for completing a probability investigation, on page 201 of Pupil Book 2. The list is also reproduced opposite.
- Go through and consider how each point applies to the example from the oral and mental starter:
  - **[Statement of topic]** Compare the abilities of teenagers and adults at probability.
  - **[Hypothesis]** 'Teenagers are better at working out theoretical probabilities than adults'.
  - **[Sample size]** Look at 30 teenagers and 30 adults. It would not be sensible to use students in your class who have just revised probability. You may even want to test a different area of mathematics if using your fellow students as a sample.
  - **[Foreseen problems]** Adults may be reluctant to answer the questions given. Choosing the sample may be difficult.
  - **[Data collection]** Record the number of correct and incorrect answers, the number of people who declined to do the questions and any other factors which may affect your results.
  - **[Analysis]** Produce statistical diagrams to compare the success rates of teenagers and adults, and calculate the experimental probability of each answering a probability question correctly.
  - **[Conclusion]** State whether you agree with initial hypothesis based on your results.

- **The class can now do Exercise 15B from Pupil Book 2, working in small groups.**

Plenary

- Having observed the students working on a choice of investigations, you may wish to give one or more groups the opportunity to present their findings so far to the rest of the class.

Checklist for completing a probability investigation

- **Specify the problem and plan**
  - ○ statement of the experiment
  - ○ hypothesis stating what you think the experiment will show
  - ○ how you will choose your sample and sample size
  - ○ any practical problems you foresee
  - ○ how you will obtain your experiment data, possibly including how to avoid bias
- **Collect data from a variety of sources**
  - ○ follow initial plan and use a suitable data-collection sheet
- **Process and represent data**
  - ○ analysis of your results comparing the experimental probabilities with theoretical probabilities
- **Interpret and discuss data**
  - ○ comparison of results with your original hypothesis
  - ○ list of any factors which might have affected your results and how you could overcome these in future
  - ○ a final conclusion

Key Words

- ☐ **hypothesis**
- ☐ **experimental data**
- ☐ **mathematical explanation**
- ☐ **statistical report**
- ☐ **experimental probability**
- ☐ **theoretical probability**

Homework

Choose one of the following tasks.

1 Complete the investigation started in the lesson by writing up the report.

2 Collect data in order to investigate the ability of teenagers and adults at working out theoretical probabilities.

3 If you have completed the report of your first investigation, then carry out and write up another detailed investigation of your own choice.

GCSE Preparation

Framework objectives – Long multiplication
Long multiplication.

Oral and mental starter

- Recall mental methods for multiplying a single-digit number by a double-digit number. For example:
  $$36 \times 7 = 30 \times 7 + 6 \times 7 = 210 + 42 = 252$$
- Using white boards to write answers on is a useful way of doing this exercise. Students should be allowed to do some jottings on these as well if they need to.
- The numbers can be generated using three 10-sided dice.

Main lesson activity

- Students have met long multiplication several times before but tend to forget the methods.
- Good number skills without a calculator will be increasingly expected at GCSE.
- Four methods are outlined below. Teachers will have to decide whether to show them all or to concentrate on one or two methods. In the Pupil Book, the box method and standard column methods are shown. Experience has shown that students have the most difficulty remembering the standard column method.
- The standard column method and the Chinese method are demonstrated in Example 1 below.

  Example 1 147×26

  Standard column method   Chinese method

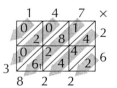

- The expanded column method and the box method are demonstrated in Example 2 below.

  Example 2 278×73

  Expanded column method   Box method

$$
\begin{array}{rl}
278 & \\
\times \ \ 73 & \\
\hline
24 & (3 \times 8) \\
210 & (3 \times 70) \\
600 & (3 \times 200) \\
560 & (70 \times 8) \\
4900 & (70 \times 70) \\
14000 & (70 \times 200) \\
\hline
20294 &
\end{array}
$$

×	200	70	8	
70	14 000	4900	560	19 460
3	600	210	24	834
				20 294

- **The class can now do Exercise 16A from Pupil Book 2 *or* Exercise 1A (page 2) from the Collins Intermediate Mathematics for GCSE textbook.**

Plenary

- Ask students to use the box method to calculate 1257×357 (= 448 749). This can be done individually, or as a class on the board.
- Explain that for GCSE they will need to be able to multiply a 3-digit by a 2-digit number without a calculator.
- As the method is generic for the product of numbers of any size, the students should feel confident that they can go beyond GCSE requirements.

Homework

Work out each of the following. Use any method you are happy with. Check your answers with a calculator afterwards.

1 216×18 2 194×46 3 223×54 4 208×67

Answers
1 3888   2 8924   3 12 042   4 13 936

Framework objectives – Long division

Long division.

Oral and mental starter

- Recall mental methods for dividing a double-digit number by a single-digit number. For example:

  $88 \div 7 = 70 \div 7 + 18 \div 7 = 10 + 2 \text{ rem } 4 = 12 \text{ rem } 4$
- Using white boards to write answers on is a useful way of doing this exercise. Students should be allowed to do some jottings on these as well if they need to.
- The numbers can be generated using three 10-sided dice.

Main lesson activity

- Students have met long division several times before but tend to forget the methods.
- Good number skills without a calculator will be increasingly expected at GCSE.
- Two methods are outlined below. Experience has shown that students have the most difficulty remembering the standard column method and achieve greater success with the chunking method.
- The standard column method is demonstrated in Example 1 below.

  Example 1 $988 \div 26$

  Go through each step of the process with the class:

$$\begin{array}{r} 38 \\ 26\overline{)988} \\ 78 \\ \hline 208 \\ 208 \\ \hline 0 \end{array}$$

Step 1: Divide 26 into 9, which does not go, then into 98. Using the 26 times table (26, 52, 78, 104, 130, 156, 182, 208, 234, 260) or good mental skills, decide how many 26s go into 98. Enter the answer of 3 and the product of 78 with the correct alignment.

Step 2: Subtract 78 from 98 to get the remainder. The link to short division can be made — that is, the remainder is written this way in the standard column method to avoid squeezing remainders into the limited space between digits.

Step 3: Bring the 8 down next to the 20 and proceed to divide 26 into 208. This gives an answer of 8, with no remainder. There are no more digits to bring down, so the calculation is complete.

The answer is 38.

- Example 2 demonstrates the method of repeated subtraction or 'chunking'.

  Example 2 $878 \div 23$

  Recall the method:

  Step 1: Write down some multiples of 23, that is:
  $10 \times 23 = 230, 20 \times 23 = 460, 5 \times 23 = 115, 2 \times 23 = 46, 3 \times 23 = 69$
  (This step is not necessary if mental skills are reasonable.)

$$\begin{array}{rl} 878 & \\ -\ 460 & (20 \times 23) \\ \hline 418 & \\ -\ 230 & (10 \times 23) \\ \hline 188 & \\ -\ 115 & (5 \times 23) \\ \hline 73 & \\ -\ 69 & (3 \times 23) \\ \hline 4 & (38 \times 23) \end{array}$$

Step 2: Repeatedly subtract as large a multiple as possible from the number until the remainder is smaller than the divisor.

Step 3: Add up how many multiples have been subtracted (38).

The answer is 38 rem 4.

- **The class can now do Exercise 16B from Pupil Book 2 *or* Exercise 1B (page 3) from the Collins Intermediate Mathematics for GCSE textbook.**

1 **a** 28 **b** 36 **c** 29 **d** 31
2 **a** 35 **b** 43 **c** 14 **d** 19
3 **a** 22 rem 21 **b** 21 rem 16 **c** 34 rem 15 **d** 19 rem 31
4 **a** 29 rem 1 **b** 51 rem 4 **c** 23 rem 18 **d** 27 rem 16

Plenary

- Ask students to use the repeated subtraction method to calculate 93.24 ÷ 3.7 (= 25.2).
- Recall the method of making the divisor into an integer (or ask the class for the method). The problem can thus be rewritten as 932.4 ÷ 37 and then worked out as normal.
- This can be done individually, or as a class on the board.
- Remind students that the method is the same but that the positioning of the decimal point is important.
- It may be worthwhile reminding students that they should estimate the answer first, when decimals are involved, to check their final answer is of the correct order of magnitude. That is, 90 ÷ 4 ≈ 22
- Repeat with similar examples such as 13.34 ÷ 5.8 (= 2.3) and 15.12 ÷ 0.24 (= 63).

Homework

Work out each of the following. Use any method you are happy with. Questions **1** and **2** have whole-number answers; **3** and **4** will give remainders.

Check your answers with a calculator afterwards.

1 990 ÷ 18 2 598 ÷ 23 3 623 ÷ 44 4 808 ÷ 27

Answers
1 55 2 26 3 14 rem 7 4 29 rem 25

LESSON 16.3

Oral and mental starter

- Recall the mental methods for multiplying and dividing a decimal, with up to two decimal places, by a single-digit integer. For example:
  $$1.61 \div 7 = 1.4 \div 7 + 0.21 \div 7 = 0.2 + 0.03 = 0.23$$
  $$1.23 \times 5 = 5 \times 1 + 5 \times 0.2 + 5 \times 0.03 = 5 + 1 + 0.15 = 6.15$$
- Using white boards to write answers on is a useful way of doing this exercise. Students should be allowed to do some jottings on these as well if they need to.
- The numbers can be generated using three 10-sided dice.

Main lesson activity

- This lesson consolidates the previous two lessons and uses long multiplication and division in practical contexts.
- Work through the example below. Examples 16.5 and 16.6 in Pupil Book 2 can also be worked through, if further practice is required.

  Example 1 The local scout troop make cakes to sell during Bob-a-Job week.
  a The scouts make 450 cakes and pack them in bags of 12. How many bags of cakes will this make and how many are left over?
  b The bags are sold for £1.25 each and the spare cakes are eaten by the troop leader. How much money does the scout troop make?

  Part **a** needs to be identified as a division: 450 ÷ 12
  This is done below by the repeated subtraction or chunking method.
  Recall the method:

  Step 1: Write down some multiples of 12, that is:
  $10 \times 12 = 120$, $20 \times 12 = 240$, $2 \times 12 = 24$, $3 \times 12 = 36$, $5 \times 12 = 60$
  (This step is not necessary if mental skills are reasonable.)

  ```
      450
  -   240   (20 × 12)
      210
  -   120   (10 × 12)
       90
  -    60   (5 × 12)
       30
  -    24   (2 × 12)
        6   (37 × 12)
  ```

  Step 2: Repeatedly subtract as large a multiple as possible from the number until the remainder is smaller than the divisor.

  Step 3: Add up how many multiples have been subtracted (37).

  The answer is 37 bags with 6 cakes left over.

  Part **b** needs to be identified as a multiplication (37×1.25).
  If the decimal point is omitted, this can be done by the normal box method, as shown below.

×	100	20	5	
30	3000	600	150	3750
7	700	140	35	875
				4625

  The decimal point is now re-introduced, checking that the final answer is of the correct order of magnitude. The answer is £46.25.

- **The class can now do Exercise 16C from Pupil Book 2 *or* Exercise 1C (page 4) from the Collins Intermediate Mathematics for GCSE textbook.**

Plenary

- Give the students some examples of multiplication and division problems, such as:

    $27 \times 134, 700 \div 28, 659 \div 36, 49 \times 49$

- Ask the class to suggest a question to go with each calculation, that puts the numbers into a real-life context.
- Now solve each of these at the board, with the students' help, or use them as homework questions.

Homework

Make up four questions, two that involve multiplication and two that involve division. Your questions must be set in a real-life context. You may have both multiplication and division as two parts of the same question.

Work out the solutions to your questions, showing all working clearly.

Framework objectives – Fractions 1

Equivalent fractions, fractions of quantities, comparing fractions.

Oral and mental starter

- Ask the class for some numbers that are multiples of both 3 and 5. If necessary write up a list of multiples for each number to help.
- Repeat this with some other pairs of small numbers.
- Now recall the methods for writing two or more fractions with a common denominator. Encourage students to try and do this in their heads. For example:

  $\frac{2}{3}$ and $\frac{4}{5}$ are the fractions $\frac{10}{15}$ and $\frac{12}{15}$ when written with a common denominator

- Now ask students to compare two fractions and put the sign <, >, or = between them. For example:

  $\frac{4}{9}$ and $\frac{5}{11}$, $\frac{3}{5}$ and $\frac{11}{13}$, $\frac{6}{7}$ and $\frac{8}{9}$, $\frac{5}{16}$ and $\frac{1}{4}$, $\frac{6}{11}$ and $\frac{7}{15}$, $\frac{8}{15}$ and $\frac{11}{18}$

- Using white boards to write answers on is a useful way of doing this exercise. Students should be allowed to do some jottings on these as well if they need to.

Main lesson activity

- This lesson recalls some basic fraction rules.
- Work through the examples below. Examples 16.7–16.10 in Pupil Book 2 can also be worked through, if further practice is required.

  Example 1 Cancel these fractions to lowest terms: **a** $\frac{24}{28}\left(=\frac{6}{7}\right)$ **b** $\frac{25}{55}\left(=\frac{5}{11}\right)$

  Explain (or get students to explain) the process of cancelling by the HCF (4 and 5 respectively in this case).

  Example 2 Which of the following fractions is larger? **a** $\frac{5}{8}$ or $\frac{2}{3}$ **b** $\frac{10}{21}$ or $\frac{8}{17}$

  In part **a** explain the process of writing the fractions with a common

  denominator (24) before comparing them $\left(\frac{15}{24}<\frac{16}{24},\text{ so }\frac{2}{3}\text{ is larger}\right)$.

  In part **b** explain that since it is not straightforward to establish the HCF of these denominators, it is faster to use a calculator to convert the fractions

  to decimals $\left(\frac{10}{21}=0.476\text{ and }\frac{8}{17}=0.471\text{ so }\frac{10}{21}\text{ is larger}\right)$.

  Example 3 What is $\frac{5}{8}$ of £960?

  Go through the process of finding $\frac{1}{8}$ of 960 (= £120) and then finding $\frac{5}{8}$ of 960,

  5 × 120 = £600.

  Example 4 In 1960 there were 4400 secondary schools in England,

  of which $\frac{3}{22}$ had female head teachers.

  In 2000 there were 4200 secondary schools in England, of which $\frac{5}{14}$ had

  female head teachers. How many more female head teachers were there in 2000 than in 1960?

  Go through the process of finding the number of female head teachers in 1960 (600) and in 2000 (1500). Hence there were 900 more in the year 2000.

- **The class can now do Exercise 16D from Pupil Book 2 _or_ Exercises 1D, 1E or 1F (pages 6–8) from the Collins Intermediate Mathematics for GCSE textbook.**

Plenary

- Write the following problems on the board.

$0.2 \times 850, \frac{1}{5}$ of 850 (both = 170), $0.44 \times 400, \frac{11}{25}$ of 400 (both = 176)

- Use these examples to discuss the connection between fractions and decimals and the advantages and disadvantages of using each when doing a calculation.
- Remind the class of the usefulness of knowing the equivalent decimals of some simple, unit fractions when doing mental calculations, that is:

$$\frac{1}{10} = 0.1, \frac{1}{2} = 0.5, \frac{1}{4} = 0.25, \frac{1}{5} = 0.2, \frac{1}{8} = 0.125$$

- If these are known, the equivalent decimals of other fractions with the same denominator can be easily worked out. Demonstrate this by asking for alternative ways to do the following:

$$\frac{17}{50} \text{ of } 600 \left(\frac{17}{50} \times 600 = 17 \times \frac{1}{10} \times \frac{1}{5} \times 600 = 17 \times 0.02 \times 600 = 0.34 \times 600 \right.$$
$$\left. = 34 \times 6 = 204 \right)$$

$$0.375 \times 88 (= 3 \times 0.125 \times 88 = \frac{3}{8} \times 88 = 33)$$

Homework

1 Cancel each of the following fractions to lowest terms.

a $\frac{18}{27}$ b $\frac{15}{24}$ c $\frac{8}{18}$

2 Fill in the missing numbers in these equivalent fractions.

a $\frac{6}{15} = \frac{\square}{75}$ b $\frac{8}{28} = \frac{\square}{21}$ c $\frac{12}{30} = \frac{8}{\square}$

3 Which of the following is larger?

a $\frac{9}{10}$ of 85 or $\frac{5}{8}$ of 120 b $\frac{7}{8}$ of 60 or $\frac{2}{3}$ of 81

4 48 000 new cars were registered in September, of which $\frac{7}{16}$ were Japanese. How many Japanese cars were registered?

Answers
1 a $\frac{2}{3}$ b $\frac{5}{8}$ c $\frac{4}{9}$
2 a $\frac{6}{15} = \frac{30}{75}$ b $\frac{8}{28} = \frac{6}{21}$ c $\frac{12}{30} = \frac{8}{20}$
3 a $\frac{9}{10}$ of 85 b $\frac{2}{3}$ of 81
4 21 000 cars

Framework objectives – Fractions 2
Addition and subtraction of fractions.

Oral and mental starter

- Using a target board as shown, point at a pair of numbers and ask students to identify the lowest common multiple.
- Students could use white boards to write their answers on.
- The numbers could also be generated using 12-sided dice (take 0 as 15 and 1 as 20).

2	3	4	5
6	7	8	9
10	12	15	20

Main lesson activity

- This is a lesson that recalls some basic fraction rules.
- Work through the examples below. Examples 16.11–16.13 in Pupil Book 2 can also be looked at, if further practice is required.

Example 1 Add together **a** $\dfrac{7}{10} + \dfrac{3}{8}$ **b** $2\dfrac{3}{5} + 1\dfrac{7}{12}$

a Explain (or get students to explain) the method of converting to fractions with the same denominator.

$$\frac{7}{10} + \frac{3}{8} = \frac{28}{40} + \frac{15}{40} = \frac{43}{40} = 1\frac{3}{40}$$

Remind students of the need to convert improper fractions in the answer to mixed numbers.

b Recall that the whole numbers can be added separately, so:

$$2 + 1 = 3 \text{ and } \frac{3}{5} + \frac{7}{12} = \frac{36}{60} + \frac{35}{60} = \frac{71}{60} = 1\frac{11}{60}$$

Hence: $2\dfrac{3}{5} + 1\dfrac{7}{12} = 3 + 1\dfrac{11}{60} = 4\dfrac{11}{60}$

Example 2 Subtract **a** $\dfrac{8}{9} - \dfrac{1}{6}$ **b** $4\dfrac{5}{8} - 1\dfrac{11}{12}$

a $\dfrac{8}{9} - \dfrac{1}{6} = \dfrac{16}{18} - \dfrac{3}{18} = \dfrac{13}{18}$

b Recall that the whole numbers can be subtracted separately, so:

$$4 - 1 = 3 \text{ and } \frac{5}{8} - \frac{11}{12} = \frac{15}{24} - \frac{22}{24} = -\frac{7}{24}$$

Hence: $4\dfrac{5}{8} - 1\dfrac{11}{12} = 3 + -\dfrac{7}{24} = 2\dfrac{17}{24}$

Example 3 In a bargain bag of tulip bulbs, $\dfrac{5}{12}$ were red tulips, $\dfrac{2}{7}$ were yellow tulips and the rest were purple. What fraction of the bulbs were purple?

This needs to be converted into an addition and subtraction problem.

$$\frac{5}{12} + \frac{2}{7} = \frac{35}{84} + \frac{24}{84} = \frac{59}{84}$$

$$1 - \frac{59}{84} = \frac{84}{84} - \frac{59}{84} = \frac{25}{84}$$

- **The class can now do Exercise 16E from Pupil Book 2 *or* Exercises 1H (page 10) from the Collins Intermediate Mathematics for GCSE textbook.**

Plenary

- Write the following problem on the board:

$$1\frac{7}{20} + 1\frac{3}{8} - 2\frac{3}{5} + 4\frac{7}{10}$$

- Discuss the best way to do this. Then work it out by whichever method is suggested.

- The answer is $4\frac{33}{40}$.

Homework

1 Work out the following. Cancel answers to lowest terms and convert into mixed numbers if necessary.

  a $\frac{1}{8} + \frac{2}{3}$ b $\frac{3}{8} + \frac{5}{6}$ c $\frac{2}{9} - \frac{1}{6}$ d $\frac{11}{12} - \frac{1}{8}$

  e $1\frac{7}{12} + 2\frac{1}{3}$ f $2\frac{5}{8} - 1\frac{1}{6}$ g $2\frac{17}{20} + 1\frac{3}{8}$ h $4\frac{7}{15} - 1\frac{5}{6}$

2 On a large estate, $\frac{5}{9}$ of the houses have two bedrooms, $\frac{1}{12}$ have five bedrooms and the rest have four bedrooms. Of the houses with two bedrooms $\frac{3}{5}$ are bungalows.

  a What fraction of the houses have four bedrooms?

  b There are 360 houses on the estate. How many two-bedroom bungalows are there?

Answers
  1 a $\frac{19}{24}$ b $1\frac{5}{24}$ c $\frac{1}{18}$ d $\frac{19}{24}$ e $3\frac{11}{12}$ f $1\frac{11}{24}$ g $4\frac{9}{40}$ h $2\frac{19}{30}$
  2 a $\frac{13}{36}$ b 120

LESSON 16.6

Framework objectives – Fractions 3

Multiplication and division of fractions.

Oral and mental starter

- Use a target board as shown.
- Point at a pair of numbers and ask students to identify their highest common factor.
- Students could use white boards to write their answers on.

Main lesson activity

- This is a lesson that recalls some more basic fraction rules.
- Work through the examples below. Examples 16.14–16.16 in Pupil Book 2 can also be looked at, if further practice is required.

Example 1 Find these products of fractions: **a** $\dfrac{6}{25} \times \dfrac{5}{8}$ **b** $2\dfrac{3}{5} \times 1\dfrac{3}{7}$

Explain (or get students to explain) the process of cancelling fractions with common factors before multiplying, and converting to improper fractions before cancelling.

Remind students that the numerators are multiplied together as are the denominators. If the original fractions have been fully cancelled, then there should be no need to cancel the answer.

a $\dfrac{6}{25} \times \dfrac{5}{8} = \dfrac{\cancel{6}^3}{\cancel{25}_5} \times \dfrac{\cancel{5}^1}{\cancel{8}_4} = \dfrac{3 \times 1}{5 \times 4} = \dfrac{3}{20}$

b $2\dfrac{3}{5} \times 1\dfrac{3}{7} = \dfrac{13}{5} \times \dfrac{10}{7} = \dfrac{13}{\cancel{5}_1} \times \dfrac{\cancel{10}^2}{7} = \dfrac{13 \times 2}{1 \times 7} = \dfrac{26}{7} = 3\dfrac{5}{7}$

Example 2 Work out these divisions: **a** $\dfrac{8}{9} \div \dfrac{1}{6}$ **b** $4\dfrac{3}{8} \div 2\dfrac{1}{12}$

Remind students of the need to turn the second fraction upside down and then multiply.

a $\dfrac{8}{9} \div \dfrac{1}{6} = \dfrac{8}{9} \times \dfrac{6}{1} = \dfrac{8}{\cancel{9}_3} \times \dfrac{\cancel{6}^2}{1} = \dfrac{8 \times 2}{3 \times 1} = \dfrac{16}{3} = 5\dfrac{1}{3}$

b $4\dfrac{3}{8} \div 2\dfrac{1}{12} = \dfrac{35}{8} \div \dfrac{25}{12} = \dfrac{\cancel{35}^7}{\cancel{8}_2} \times \dfrac{\cancel{12}^3}{\cancel{25}_5} = \dfrac{7 \times 3}{2 \times 5} = \dfrac{21}{10} = 2\dfrac{1}{10}$

Example 3 Individual tiles cover $\dfrac{2}{15}$ square metres each. How many tiles will be needed to cover an area that is $1\dfrac{3}{4}$ m by $2\dfrac{2}{3}$ m?

First we need to find the area that needs to be covered.

$1\dfrac{3}{4} \times 2\dfrac{2}{3} = \dfrac{7}{4} \times \dfrac{8}{3} = \dfrac{7}{\cancel{4}_1} \times \dfrac{\cancel{8}^2}{3} = \dfrac{7 \times 2}{1 \times 3} = \dfrac{14}{3}$

This area is then divided by the area of one tile to find out how many tiles will be needed.

$\dfrac{14}{3} \div \dfrac{2}{15} = \dfrac{14}{3} \times \dfrac{15}{2} = \dfrac{\cancel{14}^7}{\cancel{3}_1} \times \dfrac{\cancel{15}^5}{\cancel{2}_1} = \dfrac{7 \times 5}{1 \times 1} = 35$ tiles

- **The class can now do Exercise 16F from Pupil Book 2 *or* Exercises 1I and 1J (pages 11–13) from the Collins Intermediate Mathematics for GCSE textbook.**

1 a $\frac{1}{3}$ b $\frac{1}{18}$ c $\frac{3}{5}$ d $\frac{3}{10}$ e $2\frac{4}{9}$ f $1\frac{5}{8}$ g $2\frac{4}{5}$ h $2\frac{5}{8}$ i $\frac{1}{3}$ j $\frac{3}{4}$ k $7\frac{1}{2}$ l $1\frac{1}{2}$ m 6
  n $1\frac{2}{3}$ o 34 p $\frac{2}{3}$
2 $4\frac{11}{16}$ kg
3 9
4 a $2\frac{2}{3}$ cm² b 6 cm²
5 a $\frac{3}{20}$ b $\frac{4}{5}$
6 a $\frac{1}{4}$ b $\frac{1}{2}$
7 $\frac{3}{5}$
  $\frac{2}{9}$
8

Plenary

- Demonstrate the box method for multiplying mixed numbers. It is used here to find $3\frac{7}{8} \times 1\frac{2}{5}$.
- The individual products are added to give the answer:

$$3 + \frac{7}{8} + \frac{6}{5} + \frac{7}{20} = 3 + \frac{35}{40} + \frac{48}{40} + \frac{14}{40} = 3 + \frac{97}{40} = 3 + 2\frac{17}{40} = 5\frac{17}{40}$$

×	3	$\frac{7}{8}$
1	3	$\frac{7}{8}$
$\frac{2}{5}$	$\frac{6}{5}$	$\frac{7}{20}$

Homework

1 Work out each the following. Cancel down answers and write as mixed numbers where appropriate.

   a $\frac{5}{6} \times \frac{3}{25}$ b $\frac{3}{8} \div \frac{9}{16}$ c $1\frac{7}{10} \times 2\frac{1}{7}$ d $3\frac{2}{3} \div 2\frac{4}{9}$

2 On a large estate, $\frac{5}{9}$ of the houses have two bedrooms, $\frac{4}{15}$ have five bedrooms and the rest have four bedrooms. Of the houses with two bedrooms $\frac{3}{5}$ are bungalows.

   a What fraction of the houses are two-bedroom bungalows ?

   b A quarter of the four-bedroom houses are semi-detached. What fraction of the estate is four-bedroom semi-detached houses?

Answers
  1 a $\frac{1}{10}$ b $\frac{2}{3}$ c $3\frac{9}{14}$ d $1\frac{1}{2}$
  2 a $\frac{1}{3}$ b $\frac{2}{15}$

Oral and mental starter

- This activity gives some practice on mental addition and subtraction of directed numbers.
- Write some problems on the board for the students to solve, such as $-7 + -5 - -2$.
- Students could use white boards to write their answers on.
- Repeat with several more examples, sticking to numbers of 10 or less.

Main lesson activity

- This lesson recalls the rules for directed numbers.
- Work through the following examples. Examples 16.17 and 16.18 in the Pupil Book can also be looked at for extra practice.

    Example 1 Work out the following **a** $-3 - +4$ **b** $2 + -4 - -7$

    c $-4 \times +4$ **d** $-2 \times +6 \div -3$

    Remind the class that when two signs occur together, two alike signs combine to make a single plus sign ($+ + = +$ and $- - = +$), whilst two unlike signs combine to make a single minus sign ($+ - = -$ and $- + = -$). Hence:

    a $-3 - +4 = -3 - 4$

    Once any adjacent signs have been combined, the total can be worked out by counting along a number line: start at zero and count left for negative numbers and right for positive numbers. Hence:

    $-3 - 4 = -7$

    b $2 + -4 - -7 = 2 - 4 + 7 = 5$

    Now remind the class of the rules for multiplying (or dividing) positive and negative numbers. Once again, two alike signs combine to make a positive number ($+ \_ + = +$ and $- \_ - = +$), whilst two unlike signs combine to make a negative number ($+ \_ - = -$ and $- \_ + = -$). Hence:

    c $-4 \times +4 = -16$

    In part **d**, they also need to remember to work from left to right.

    d $-2 \times +6 \div -3 = -12 \div - 3 = +4$

    Example 2 When $a = -3$, $b = -5$ and $c = +4$, evaluate the following algebraic expressions.

    a $(a - b)c$ **b** $a^2 + b \times (c + a)$

    Encourage students to first substitute the numbers into the expression, using brackets for clarity.

    a $(a - b)c = ((-3) - (-5)) \times (+4) = (-3 + 5) \times 4 = 2 \times 4 = 8$

    b $a^2 + b \times (c + a) = (-3)^2 + (-5) \times ((+4) + (-3)) = 9 + -5 \times 1 = 9 - 5 = 4$

- **The class can now do Exercise 16G from Pupil Book 2 *or* Exercises 1K and 1L (pages 15–16) from the Collins Intermediate Mathematics for GCSE textbook.**

1   a −4   b −12   c +11   d +7   e −12   f +20   g +4   h −4   i +8   j +3
    k −4   l +16   m −5   n +5   o −5
2   a +1   b −2   c −4 or −8
3   a +4   b −2
4   a +2   b −12
5   a 1.5   b −4
6   a +8   b −0.5
7   a +21   b −4.5
8   a 25   b +7   c +36   d +72   e −96   f −54
9   (Other answers are possible)   a +7 + −5   b −3 − −5   c −5 − −3   d −3 + −2
10   (Other answers are possible)   a −2 × −6   b +4 ÷ −2   c −6 × +4 ÷ −2
                d +8 ÷ +4 × −3

Plenary

- Discuss situations where directed numbers occur in Algebra, such as:
$$-2(x - 3) = -2x + 6 \text{ and } -6x - -2x = -6x + 2x = -4x$$
- Go through some more examples of these, such as:
$$-3(2y - x) \, (= -6y + 3x) \text{ and } 5y - +3y \, (= +2y)$$
- Ask for the expansion of $-(3 - 2x)$. Students find this a difficult concept. For those who have difficulty, explain that it can be thought of as $-1(3 - 2x) = -1 \times 3 + -1 \times -2x = -3 + 2x$. The majority of students should be happy with this method of writing in the coefficient of 1.

Homework

1   Work out the following.

    a −4 − 6   b +3 − −7   c −3 × −4

    d +32 ÷ −4   e −6 × −6 ÷ −4   f $(-5)^2 - -4$

    g $(-3 - 1) \times -2$ h $(5 - -1)^2 - 12$

2   You are told that $a = -2$, $b = +3$ and $c = -4$. Work out the value of:

    a $c^2 - b^2$ b $(2a - b)(3a + b)$ c $5(a + 2b) - 3(b - 2c)$

Answers
1   a −10   b +10   c +12   d −8   e −9   f +29   g +8   h +24
2   a +7   b +21   c −13

LESSON 16.8

Oral and mental starter

- Remind students that a percentage increase or decrease can be performed easily if the multiplier is known. Give some examples where students must identify the multiplier for a given percentage increase or decrease and vice versa, such as:
    1.34 is a 34% increase, 0.78 is a 22% decrease, a 12% increase is 1.12, a 2% decrease is 0.98
- Students could use white boards to write their answers on.

Main lesson activity

- Introduce the students to the 'road-sign' for percentage calculations, as shown on the right.
- Once a percentage has been expressed as a multiplier, this triangle can be used to do all of the usual percentage calculations. Demonstrate how to use it with the examples below.

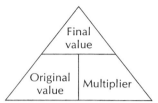

Example 1 A pair of jeans is reduced in a sale by 15%. They originally cost £35.80.

What is the cost after the reduction?

The quantity required is the Final value (the cost after reduction). Covering this up on the road-sign shows that it is calculated by multiplying the Original value by the Multiplier.

Ask students to work out the multiplier for a 15% decrease (0.85). Hence the Final value is:

£35.80 × 0.85 = £30.43

Example 2 Bernice scored 33 out of 60 on a test. What is her mark as a percentage?

We need to find out the Multiplier. The road-sign shows that this is calculated by dividing the Final value by the Original value.

33 ÷ 60 = 0.55

Converting this multiplier to a percentage shows that Bernice scored 55%.

Example 3 After a 20% increase John's hourly wage is now £6.72. What was it before the increase?

Ask students to identify the values that we know — £6.72 is the final value and the multiplier is 1.2.

According to the road sign the Original value is the Final value ÷ Multiplier = £6.72 ÷ 1.2 = £5.60.

- **The class can now do Exercise 16H from Pupil Book 2 *or* Exercises 2B–G (pages 32–41) from the Collins Intermediate Mathematics for GCSE textbook.**

1 **a** £85.80   **b** £128.40   **c** 682.5 g   **d** 62.1 m   **e** £111.25   **f** 156 km
2 **a** £48.60   **b** 87.4 kg   **c** £360   **d** 57.8 m   **e** £112.50   **f** 235.2 cm
3 £10 625
4 **a** 60%   **b** 68%   **c** 28%   **d** 92%   **e** 70%   **f** 51%
5 £6.00 per hour
6 £1102.50
7 **a** £109.76   **b** 754.65 g   **c** £702   **d** 51.04 m   **e** £99.88   **f** 320.76 cm
8 **a** £99.36   **b** 795.4 g   **c** £399.36   **d** £56.32   **e** £130.65   **f** 148.48 cm
9 £218.24
10 **a** 30%   **b** 60%   **c** 70%   **d** 70%   **e** 80%   **f** 60%
11 75 kg
12 £1208.03

Plenary

- Ask the class if they can demonstrate that an $x\%$ increase of a quantity, followed by an $x\%$ decrease of the new quantity does not take you back to the original quantity.
- This could be shown by a 20% increase of 100 (to give 120), followed by a 20% decrease of 120 (to give 96).
- Make sure that students understand the idea of the multiplier, which means that the simplified calculation is $100 \times 1.2 \times 0.8 = 96$
- Cover some more examples, such as 10% ($100 \times 1.1 \times 0.9 = 99$), 30% ($100 \times 1.3 \times 0.7 = 91$), 40% ($100 \times 1.4 \times 0.6 = 84$) and 50% ($100 \times 1.5 \times 0.5 = 75$).
- It should become clear to the students that an $x\%$ increase followed by an $x\%$ decrease will always result in a smaller quantity than was started with.

Homework

1 A suit normally costing £250 is reduced by 15%. What does it cost now?

2 Work out the percentage that the first number is of the second.

   a 26 out of 50   **b** 7 out of 20   **c** 84 out of 200

3 After a 5% wage increase, Bertram now earns £9.45 per hour. What did she earn before?

4 At the start of 1997, Roger put £2000 in a savings account. The account pays 10% compound interest per year. How much is in the account at the start of 1999?

Answers
1 £212.50
2 **a** 52%   **b** 35%   **c** 42%
3 £9.00
4 £2420

Oral and mental starter

- This activity gives students a brief introduction to solving simultaneous equations.
- Explain that if you have two unknowns in one equation, then it generally can't be solved, but if you have two equations containing the same two unknowns, then they can generally be solved. One way to do this is to subtract one equation from the other, so that some of the terms cancel out. Demonstrate this with the two equations shown below.

$$3x - 5y = 16 \quad - \textbf{i}$$
$$3x - 6y = 15 \quad - \textbf{ii}$$

- Explain that you want to take away equation **ii** from equation **i**. Do this by subtracting the like terms individually. Point out that no terms should be taken over the equals sign.

$$
\begin{array}{ccc}
3x & -5y & 16 \\
-\ 3x & -\ -6y & -\ 15 \\
\hline
0 & +y & +1
\end{array}
$$

So $\quad 0 + y = +1$
$$y = 1$$

- Highlight how the terms in x have cancelled, so that only one unknown is left, which enables the equation to be solved. If desired, the value of x could also be worked out, by substituting $y = 1$ back into equation **i** or **ii** ($x = 7$).
- Repeat with another example:

$$2x - 5y = 6 \quad - \textbf{iii}$$
$$4x - 5y = 10 \quad - \textbf{iv}$$

- This time the required order of subtraction is (**iv**)–(**iii**). Work through this to give $2x = 4$, $x = 2$.
- Again, y could also be calculated once x is known ($y = -0.4$).

Main lesson activity

- This lesson will remind students of some of the basic rules of algebra.
- Many of the ideas can be covered by manipulating expressions such as $2(x + 3) - 3(x - 1)$.
- Work through some examples like this. Some suggestions are given below.

   Example 1 Expand and simplify the following expressions.

   $\quad$ **a** $2(x + 3) - 3(x - 1)$ $\quad$ **b** $4(2x - 3) + 3(x - 6)$

   In this example, make sure that students know how to expand brackets, multiply negative numbers together and collect like terms.

   a $2(x + 3) - 3(x - 1) = 2x + 6 - 3x + 3 = -x + 9$
   b $4(2x - 3) + 3(x - 6) = 8x - 12 + 3x - 18 = 11x - 30$

   Example 2 Expand and simplify: $x(2x - y) - 2x(y - x)$
   In this example make sure students are able to work with powers and collect like terms.

   $\quad x(2x - y) - 2x(y - x) = 2x^2 - xy - 2xy + 2x^2 = 4x^2 - 3xy$

   Example 3 Solve the equation: $3(x - 2) + 2(x + 1) = 11$
   In this example make sure students are able to solve the resulting equation and that they understand the difference between an expression and an equation.

$$
\begin{aligned}
3(x - 2) + 2(x + 1) &= 11 \\
3x - 6 + 2x + 2 &= 11 \\
5x - 4 &= 11 \\
5x &= 15 \\
x &= 3
\end{aligned}
$$

Example 4 Solve this equation: $5(2x - 3) = 3(x + 2) + 7$

In this example, make sure that students know to collect the x terms on the left hand side and the number terms on the right hand side before solving the equation.

$$5(2x - 3) = 3(x + 2) + 7$$
$$10x - 15 = 3x + 6 + 7$$
$$10x - 3x = 15 + 6 + 7$$
$$7x = 28$$
$$x = 4$$

● **The class can now do Exercise 16I from Pupil Book 2 *or* some of the basic techniques of algebra can be practised using the exercises in Chapter 6 of the Collins Intermediate Mathematics for GCSE textbook.**

Exercise 16I Answers

1 **a** $5x - 2$ **b** $x - 9$ **c** $-x + 26$ **d** $2x + 40$ **e** $13x - 11$ **f** $-3x - 12$ **g** $2x^2 - xy$
  h $-5xy$ **i** $3x^2 - 11xy$ **j** $11x^2 - 8xy$
2 **a** 4 **b** 28 **c** 5 **d** 3.5 **e** −1 **f** −2 **g** 0 **h** 2 **i** −1 **j** −1.5
3 **a** 2 **b** 5 **c** 1.5 **d** 1.5 **e** −2 **f** 2.5
4 25
5 2.5

GCSE Question Answers

1 **a** 2 **b** 0.3 **c** −1.5
2 **a** £35.70 **b** £18.40
3 £624.32
4 **a i** $3x$ **ii** $3a + 2b$ **b** $3a + 6$
  c $8x + 1$
5 **a** 18p **b** £6.48 **c** 75%

6 **a** 1.8 **b** 15
7 **a** 20% **b** 80 minutes
8 **a** 6 **b** 12
9 $14x - 13$
10 **a i** 8 **ii** 6 **b** −1, −5
11 99p

Plenary

● Write the following expression on the board:
$$\frac{x - 1}{3} + \frac{x + 3}{2}$$
● Ask students if they can simplify this. There are two methods.
● The first method is to write it out as fractions with a common denominator, that is:
$$\frac{2(x - 1)}{6} + \frac{3(x + 3)}{6} = \frac{2x - 2 + 3x + 9}{6} = \frac{5x + 7}{6}$$
● The alternative is to divide through by the denominators, that is:
$$\frac{x}{3} - \frac{1}{3} + \frac{x}{2} + \frac{3}{2} = \left[\frac{1}{3} + \frac{1}{2}\right]x - \frac{1}{3} + \frac{3}{2} = \frac{5}{6}x + \frac{7}{6}$$

Published by HarperCollins*Publishers* Limited
77–85 Fulham Palace Road
Hammersmith
London
W6 8JB

Browse the complete Collins catalogue at
www.collinseducation.com

© HarperCollins*Publishers* Ltd 2003

10 9 8 7 6 5 4

ISBN 0 00 713867 9

Keith Gordon, Kevin Evans, Trevor Senior and Brian Speed assert their moral rights to be identified as the authors of this work.

British Library Cataloguing in Publication Data
A Catalogue record for this publication is available from the British Library

Edited by John Day
Typesetting and design by Gray Publishing
Project Management by Sam Holmes and Marie Taylor
Covers by Tim Byrne
Illustrations by Gray Publishing
Additional proofreading by Amanda Whyte
CD mastering by Alan Trewartha
Production by Sarah Robinson
Printed and bound by Martins the Printers, Berwick upon Tweed

The publishers would like to thank the many teachers and advisers whose feedback helped to shape *Maths Frameworking*.

Every effort has been made to trace copyright holders and to obtain their permission for the use of copyright material. The author and publishers will gladly receive any information enabling them to rectify any error or omission in subsequent editions.

You might also like to visit:
www.harpercollins.co.uk
The book lover's website